B

Barty Dobbs is always being teased about his size, but after watching canoeists on the river, he is determined to overcome all obstacles and join the local canoe club. With the support of his new friend, Dan, Barty discovers that he has a talent for canoeing. Then comes the weekend of the slalom race. Has Barty taken on too much? Or is this his chance to show everyone just what he can do?

JANET COLLINS

BARTY

A Magnet Book

For the members of the Telford Canoe Club

First published in 1986
by Blackie and Son Ltd
This Magnet edition first published in 1987
by Methuen Children's Books Ltd
11 New Fetter Lane, London EC4P 4EE
Copyright © 1986 Janet Collins
Printed in Great Britain by
Richard Clay Ltd, Bungay, Suffolk

ISBN 0 416 01152 7

Contents

1

End of Term

Amanda Parsons' clear high voice announced, "Barty
Dobbs can't go camping because he wets the bed."

Barty felt all the eyes of Class 2 turn towards him.
His face went red and hot. He looked at the table-
top and wished he could disappear. Miss Swan said,
"Lots of people can't go camping with us, Amanda,
for lots of reasons."

"I'm going to Spain," said Ruth Charters. "So I
can't go camping either."

"I'm going to Wales in a caravan *and* I'm going
camping with the school," said Nikki Felton.

"Aren't you lucky," said Miss Swan. She smiled
at Class 2 and continued with what she had been
saying before Amanda made her nasty remark. Barty
went on looking at the table-top, his eyes full of
tears. It was perfectly true—he did wet the bed quite
often. It was also true that he was very, very small
for a nine-year-old and that his growth was restricted. Miss Swan sometimes called him 'Porgy'. She
said it stood for 'Person of Restricted Growth'. The
way she said it sounded kind and made Barty smile.
Poor Barty. He had been hoping everyone would
think his parents could not afford to send him to
camp because his Dad was out of work.

That Mandy Parsons! She lived near Barty, and
her Mum and Barty's Mum often chatted together.
Mrs Parsons' face always had 'That Look' on it when

she caught sight of Barty. Grown-ups often had 'That Look' when Barty was around. It expressed a mixture of pity and dislike; pity because he was small and adopted, and dislike because he was ugly and he wet the bed. Barty thought he was used to it. He thought he didn't mind any more. Mum always said that he was her special boy and that he should keep his chin up and not care. He tried. He really tried—but then that Mandy Parsons had to tell. Now the whole class knew.

"And I want you all to write a journal," said Miss Swan. Barty looked up. He hadn't heard a word that Miss Swan had said.

"What's a journal, Miss?" asked Brian Duffy.

"It's like a diary. You write in it every day," said Miss Swan. "But you can draw in it too, or stick photographs in it and other souvenirs."

"What shall I stick in it, Miss Swan?" said Ruth, making sure everyone knew that her holiday was going to be different from theirs.

"Why don't you save everything with Spanish writing on it?" suggested Miss Swan. "You can collect sweet papers and food labels and tickets, and things like that."

"Shall I collect Welsh words on things?" said Nikki. "Shall I learn to speak some Welsh?"

"What a good idea," said Miss Swan.

"Barty can't keep a journal," said the rotten Amanda. "He never goes anywhere, not even for the day."

"He doesn't need to," said Miss Swan. "He lives in such a beautiful place. Every day must be like a holiday."

Barty looked at her. Suddenly he *loved* Miss Swan.

She was nice, and pretty. She always smelt of flowers when he went out to read to her, and now she had just told the whole class that he lived in a lovely place. Barty smiled at her.

The bell went for Afternoon Play. Class 2 streamed out of the classroom and into the sunshine. Barty waited until last.

"Barty," said Miss Swan, "would you like to help me tidy the cupboard instead of going out to play?"

Barty looked out of the window. Amanda had a group of her cronies around her.

"That dwarf!" he heard her say spitefully.

"Yes, Miss," said Barty. "What shall I do first?"

It was nearly the end of term. Miss Swan was taking some of Class 2 and Class 1 camping with Mr Pugh, the teacher of the top class. She wanted to leave everything tidy at the end of term, so there was a lot to do. Barty stacked books and boxes of apparatus. He tidied the drawing paper and washed the paint trays. Miss Swan was always surprised at how strong he was in spite of his size.

"I meant it, you know," said Miss Swan. "You do live in a place where people would like to spend their holidays. You're very lucky. Don't mind what Amanda says. She's a silly girl."

"Oh, I know," said Barty. "My Mum says she's spoiled rotten. It's all right, Miss, about the camping and all that. One good thing about my Dad being out of work—he's around in the holidays. We've got an allotment as well as our back yard. We're growing vegetables. He's going to take me fishing sometimes, too."

"That's nice," said Miss Swan. "And you must

still write a journal. Write it for me, and do some of your lovely drawings."

"And stick in some of my sweet papers?" asked Barty, grinning.

"Barty, I think you are making fun of me," said Miss Swan, as Class 2 clattered in from the playground.

"Teacher's pet!" hissed Amanda.

"Snake!" Barty hissed back.

"I'd rather be a snake than a midget—ow!" Amanda yelled as Miss Swan pulled her plaits.

"If you behave like this in camp I shall put a snake in your tent," said Miss Swan. Amanda was silent. Miss Swan looked as if she really meant it.

Miss Swan opened a packet of new, shiny red notebooks. They had blank pages for drawings in between the writing pages. Everybody got one, including Barty.

"Write your name on the cover," said Miss Swan, "and then you can copy the word 'Journal' from the blackboard. You can decorate the covers however you like. Best writing, mind."

They took until home-time to decorate the covers, and then Class 2 said goodbye to Miss Swan and filed out, clutching their journals. Barty went home by car. This made him angry, because it proved that he was different. Amanda Parsons walked home to the same street in the same village, but the Education Office said that Barty was handicapped and so he had a volunteer driver every day to drive him to and from school. Miss Swan was glad. She was afraid that he might be bullied if he walked home. He had no big brothers or sisters to stick up for him.

Today's volunteer was Miss Sangster. She was

tall, with a suntanned face and always smelt of horses.

"Hello, Barty," she said. "Had a good day?"

Barty told her about the journal on the way home. Miss Sangster said, "Super!" She always said, "Super!" whatever you told her. Barty thought that one day he would tell her the Martians had landed on the playground. How he would laugh to hear her say, "Super!" to that.

2

Making Plans

Barty went in the back way. Mum had been baking. A tray of cakes was cooling on a rack. He took one, and then as Mum couldn't see him, he stretched out to take another.

"Just one cake, Barty," came his mother's voice. She was upstairs.

"Yes, Mum, thanks," called Barty, as he put the red journal on the dresser.

"Come up and get changed," she called. Barty stumped up the stairs, which were quite steep. As he washed and changed he told his Mum about Amanda Parsons. He hadn't meant to, but he still felt bad inside about it. His Mum sat down on the bed beside him.

"That Amanda. She doesn't know anything. It's not your fault, Barty. You'll grow out of it. You're not as bad as you were." Mum smoothed down a tuft of his hair. "We'll ask Dr Chowdhari about it when we go to the clinic. Don't worry, Barty."

"I won't," he replied. "Who wants to go camping, anyway? Just think of having to eat breakfast with Amanda Parsons!"

Mum laughed. "Oh, our Barty, go on with you."

Barty slipped off the bed and padded out. Mrs Dobbs sighed. Her adopted son had more than his share of problems, but he was a proper little joker. He had been nearly battered to death by his real parents before she and Ted had adopted him—an ugly little scrap of a child. Ted had said, "He'll take a bit of loving, that one."

"Well, we've got no others. I'll get him strong and well," his wife had replied, years ago, and so she had. She looked out of the window. Amanda Parsons was skipping with some of her friends. Mrs Parsons was chatting to a neighbour by her gate. "Right!" thought Barty's Mum. "I'll just go and give that young lady a piece of my mind." She pulled her cardigan round her. "I won't be long, Barty," she called.

Barty went and looked out of his bedroom window. He saw his Mum talking to Mrs Parsons. Amanda had stopped skipping. It didn't look too friendly. Barty began to wish he hadn't told his Mum what Amanda had said. Then he grinned. Mrs Parsons slapped Amanda's leg, just below the short flowery dress. Mrs Dobbs turned and walked home triumphant.

Over tea Barty's Dad said, "What's this then, on the dresser? 'Bartholomew Dobbs' Journal'. My word, that looks posh!"

Barty explained about the journal and how it was to be in a competition after the holidays. He told his Dad what Miss Swan had said about his lovely home by the river.

"We've got an old camera somewhere," said Mum. "I reckon if we got a film you could take some photographs for the journal."

"And you're good at drawing, young Barty," said Dad. "It will give you an interest, won't it?"

After tea Dad went out to his old van. It was really very old and needed lots of repairs. Dad did all the work himself. Barty went out to watch.

"What's wrong with it, Dad?"

"I reckon it's the carburettor this time," said Dad.

"Can you mend it?" asked Barty.

"No. I'll just have to get a spare," said Dad. Barty was pleased about that, because it meant a visit to the scrap yard to get a spare from a van that was going to be smashed up.

"We'll go to Charlie's yard when the holiday starts," said Dad. He wiped his dirty hands and set off for his allotment. Barty put his hands in his pockets just like Dad and followed him. They inspected their rows of vegetables, picked off some caterpillars and sprayed for greenfly. Then they saw Mr Parsons on his allotment and went over to talk to him. Mr Parsons was sitting by his strawberry patch. He had brought a big jug of cider to his garden hut and he offered some to Barty's Dad.

"Help yourself to strawberries, Barty," he said. "There should still be a few left." As Barty stooped along the rows Mr Parsons talked to his Dad in a low voice. He had 'That Look' on his face. Dad burst out laughing. He didn't worry about things as much as Mum. All he ever said was, "Barty's all right. He'll grow out of it," when Mum got into a state about Barty's latest problem. As long as Barty was healthy and doing his best at school his Dad really believed that the other little problems would disappear, given time.

"That Amanda!" chuckled Dad. "She'll have to learn to watch her tongue!"

"Good of you to take it like that," mumbled Mr Parsons.

3

The Clinic

As it happened, Barty didn't see the awful Amanda again that term because on the last day of school he had to go for his check-up at the hospital. Because the van was still broken down he and his Mum had to go on three different buses. The appointment and the journey there and back took them all day.

Dr Chowdhari was a specialist in children's growth problems. He had soft black hair, a brown skin and tiny, gentle hands. His eyes twinkled behind his thick glasses and he had a voice that sounded like singing to Barty.

In the waiting room there were some familiar faces, but there were also some mothers and toddlers that Barty hadn't seen before. There was a little girl, about three years old, dressed in a pretty pink dress that did nothing to disguise her fat little legs. She had her face buried in her mother's skirt, and her mother looked miserable and worried.

Barty's Mum slid along the row of seats to sit beside her. She always tried to speak to some of the new mothers at the clinic, because she remembered her first visits with Barty, and how worried she used to be. While they chatted Barty looked at the little girl, with her big head and short legs. "She's as ugly as me," he thought, but then the little girl, hearing voices, turned round. Her eyes were a deep blue, enormous in her chubby face, and she had such pretty hair. The beautiful eyes filled with tears. Barty pulled a funny face at her and she giggled. He found some wrapped barley sugar in his pocket and gave her a piece. She slid to the floor where she and Barty sat playing finger games until Barty was called to go and get undressed.

"Goodbye," said the new mother, picking up her little girl. "Your boy is a credit to you."

"Good luck," said Mum. "She'll be fine. You just wait and see."

Dr Chowdhari had two students with him. They read Barty's notes, measured him, weighed him and even measured the size of his head. Dr Chowdhari made ink marks down his spine. Barty touched his toes, twisted to the side, did sit-ups and even press-ups, just as if he was having a PE lesson. Then he went for an X-ray, wearing a hospital gown, and for a blood test. Then he had to blow up balloons while they listened to his chest. All the time Dr Chowdhari spoke in his soft voice, making little jokes and explaining things to Mum and the students. Barty's Mum stayed for a private word while Barty went to get dressed.

"All right?" said Barty as his Mum took his hand to leave.

"Fine, Barty, just fine," she replied.

"Goodbye, Bartholomew. You'll grow to be nearly as tall as me," said Dr Chowdhari. He was about five feet four inches tall.

"Then I couldn't act R2D2, or join the circus," laughed Barty. It was their joke every time at the clinic.

Mum bought Barty an ice-cream while they waited for the bus.

"I'll be glad when Dad gets that old van fixed," she grumbled. "All this standing gets to my legs."

"Did you tell that lady with the little girl about me?" asked Barty.

"Yes, I didn't think you'd mind," said Mum. "You see, Barty, I'm proud of you. I tell everybody what a battered scrap you were when Dad and I came to get you, and then they look at you and see how sturdy you are now. It helps the mothers when they see you doing well."

"I know," said Barty, "but I wish—"

"What?"

"I just wish that you'd talk about something else, like I'm a champion jockey or a genius, or something," mumbled Barty.

"Well, you're not," said Mum. "Are you? So I can't say that."

One day, thought Barty, one day I'll be something special. Then she'll see! He and his Dad often used to talk about his future. Sometimes it was hard to imagine himself doing anything, but Dad said being small could be a good thing in some jobs.

"You can't be in the Horse Guards or the police," Dad would say, "but you can be a jockey or an engineer." They made lists like 'Tinker, tailor, soldier, sailor...' and crossed off the impossible ones.

"It's brains that count in the end," said Dad, "not size."

Once back home, Barty decided he would start his journal by writing about the clinic. Miss Swan would be interested in that. He drew a picture of the little girl with the blue eyes and he drew his own back view with ink splodges on it. He couldn't spell

'Chowdhari' and had to ask his Mum. He wrote about the students, the cheerful tea ladies and the long, long bus journey. He was quite pleased with the first pages.

4

Charlie's Yard

When, the next morning, Barty saw his old dungarees and a T-shirt on the end of his bed, he wriggled
with pleasure. No more school for six whole weeks!
Then he wriggled again, cautiously. His sheets were
quite dry. When his Mum came up to make the beds
she would be pleased. Barty always had to strip his
own bed on a Disaster Day. He didn't mind. It was
only fair to his Mum, who had to do all the extra
washing. But today was a really good day.

The next nice thing that happened was at breakfast.
His Dad said, "I reckon we'll go to Charlie's Yard
today, to try and find a carburettor." It was a long
walk to Charlie's Yard, but Barty didn't mind.

There were piles of broken cars everywhere in the
scrap yard. Charlie had a machine that crushed them
into cubes of crumpled metal. Then a crane put the
cubes on a lorry, and they were taken away to be
recycled. Charlie kept the usable parts for people like
Barty's Dad, and saved the wheels and the tyres.
Most of the tyres went off to be made into doormats,
but Charlie used some of them himself to make plant
pots. He slit them, turned them inside out and filled
them with soil. All round his office he had old tyre
plant pots painted white and filled with flowers.
When Barty and his Dad had said hello, and admired
the pots, Charlie said Barty could make one for his
Mum if he liked.

Dad explained about the carburettor trouble. Charlie yelled for Sid, one of his sons, and Dad and Sid went over together to a row of old vans. Barty stood by the office to watch the crusher, operated by Charlie's other son, Des. He had to stand quite still, because the crusher was dangerous. But it was great to watch. Des switched off and came over. He picked Barty up and swung him high in the air.

"Started training for the Grand National yet?" he said. Barty giggled. Des was over six feet tall. He let Barty ride on his shoulders into the office, ducking down at the door. Charlie poured mugs full of strong, sweet tea out of a dirty tea pot. Then Dad came in with a usable carburettor.

"How much?" asked Dad.

"That's OK, mate," replied Charlie. "Glad to help."

"Well, if you're sure," said Dad, "but that's no way to run a business, giving things away."

"All right, then," said Charlie. "Bring me some home-grown spuds from your allotment next time."

"Fine," said Dad.

"Any problems with that, just ring us up," said Charlie.

Barty and his Dad started the long walk home. A horn sounded. It was Sid. He had a lorry-load of scrap to deliver, so he gave Barty and his Dad a lift nearly all the way home.

"See you fishing some time," yelled Sid, as he roared off in the lorry.

Mum was pleased about the old tyre Barty had brought home to make into a plant pot. She said it would look nice when it was finished. That night she looked over his shoulder as he wrote his journal.

He drew the crusher, and Charlie's plant pots filled with flowers. Then he drew a lorry and the crane, and wrote about recycling the bits of broken cars. Mum thought he had done very well.

"I'll have to get you some crayons," she remarked. "Those drawings will look better if they're coloured."

"I reckon nobody else will have been to a scrap yard for their holidays," laughed Dad.

5

On the Riverbank

Barty's Dad spent the next day working on the van, but the day after that he felt like getting some fresh air, so he and Barty decided to go fishing. Mum had made some bread pudding from a stale loaf, and they also had a flask of tea, some pop for Barty and some sandwiches. In a green plastic tub they had put some wriggly maggots which Dad had bought at the fishing tackle shop.

"Mind you don't mix up your bread pudding with those maggots," laughed Mum. "Ugh! Aren't they horrible!"

Dad and Barty set off. Dad had a big basket with a lid to hold all his things. Barty had a green knapsack on his back.

The best fishing spot was only yards from their house. They had to go through a gate by the roadside, and along a footpath by the river bank. The path had been worn smooth by the feet of hundreds of fishermen. At various places along the bank there were gaps in the reeds and weeds, which led right down to the water's edge. Dad called these places 'pegs'. On competition days, each peg had a number and an angler could fish from that spot only. At weekends each peg was occupied, but on weekdays there were very few anglers about. Today, Tom Cowden, who worked on shifts at the power station, was there with his salmon rod. He had a special licence to catch salmon. Dad said he was the best fisherman on this part of the river.

"Morning, Tom," said Barty's Dad. "What's it like, then?"

"River's dropping," said Tom. "There's a salmon resting over there. He doesn't want to know about my worm, though."

"Why is he resting?" asked Barty.

"He's come up from the sea," said Tom. "He was born in this river, and he has swum home so that his children can be born here as well."

"Will he go back to the sea, then?" asked Barty

"Ha! He will if I don't catch him, or if he doesn't die after they've spawned," said Tom, looking at the deep pool where the salmon lay.

"Why might he die?" asked Barty.

"The salmon get very tired coming up river, swimming over weirs and through eddies, against the rapids and through the shallows. Then it's very hard work making a scrape and laying eggs, like it is having a baby," said Tom.

"Then they might get caught by an otter or another fisherman further up river, or poisoned by all the river pollution. It's a cruel life, right enough," said Barty's Dad.

"I won't try to catch him," said Barty.

"You haven't got a licence. You stick to your tiddlers, young Barty," said Tom.

"We're going down river a bit, to peg number eight," said Barty's Dad.

"We've got bread pudding," called Barty, as they walked on.

"My, my!" called Tom after them. "Reckon I'll join you for lunch."

"You're welcome," said Barty's Dad. "See you later."

When they reached peg number eight, Barty slithered down the bank to the water's edge. There was a shelf of rock jutting out into the water where he liked to fish. Dad passed him the rods and the stools. He helped Barty to set up his rod, with line and weights and a hook.

"Be careful with the spare line and weights," he said. "All your bits must go back in your bag. If a duck or a swan should swallow them, it could die."

"I'll be careful," promised Barty.

It was very quiet and peaceful by the river. There was the sound of the rippling and eddying of the water. Birds were singing in the trees on the riverside. A family of ducks swam past them. The ducklings were almost fully grown. Gulls flapped lazily up and down. A crow cawed from the top of the hill. A woodpecker drummed on a tree. Barty's Dad could name all the birds and flowers. Every time Barty said, "What's that?" his Dad could tell him.

Barty wandered off by himself for a little while, and saw the most amazing thing. There was a little brown bird walking across *the bottom* of the river— actually under water! Over the stones it ran, with the river flowing over its head.

"Dad! Dad!" called Barty, running back. "There's a little bird. You must come and see!"

"I should think you've scared it away," scolded Dad. "You mustn't make that row."

"Sorry," whispered Barty. "Dad, I saw a little bird. It could walk under water. It wasn't a duck."

"How big was it?" asked Dad. He thought he knew what the bird was, but he wanted Barty to

24

notice things carefully. Barty showed the size and shape of the amazing bird with his hands.

"It looked brownish, with some white on it," said Barty.

"That's the dipper," said Dad. "We're lucky to see him, because he only likes places where the river is clean and fast-running."

"Oh," said Barty. He blinked suddenly at a flash of blue, as a kingfisher darted past. "I wish he would stay still," he said. "I've never seen him standing still."

"He's like you then," laughed Dad. "To see the kingfisher on his branch, you have to be really quiet and patient. Then he'll perch by you and catch more minnows than you can."

"That's easy," said Barty. "I can't catch anything."

Tom came along the path and they shared their lunch. Tom's wife had made him a big pasty, and he swapped some of that for a piece of bread pudding. Barty offered him a banana, but he didn't want that. They chatted quietly while they ate and drank, enjoying the dappled shade beneath the trees. Barty really enjoyed being with Dad and his friends. They never seemed to have 'That Look' on their faces when Barty was around. Instead, they took time to show him how to bait his hook with wriggly maggots, untangled his line for him when he got in a muddle, and pulled him out of the water when he fell in.

"Perhaps it's only fishermen who are so nice and friendly," thought Barty. He knew from the newspapers that cruel, nasty things happened in the world—but not by *his* river.

★ ★ ★

They all baited their hooks again in the afternoon, but nobody had any luck. Tom's salmon left its pool and leapt high in the air on its journey up river, but Tom didn't mind. He packed away his rod, for he had to go to work that evening. Barty and his Dad went home in the late afternoon. They hadn't caught even a minnow or a stickleback, but it had been a good day.

As they walked home along the riverside they heard voices. Three strange creatures dressed in bright orange were splashing along by the bank on the other side of the river. They actually turned out to be three big boys in orange life-jackets and white helmets, paddling canoes. One of them climbed out on the bank and tipped water out of his canoe. The other two boys were laughing at him. They called out to each other in croaky gruff voices, not quite men's but not children's either. Barty stared at them. They seemed so tall, and so happy.

"Looks interesting, eh, Barty?" said Dad.

"Why are they laughing so much?" asked Barty. "I don't see anything funny."

"That boy on the bank must have fallen in," said Dad.

"You'd think that would make him cry," said Barty.

"Oh, no. It's all part of the fun," said Dad. "They need to be good swimmers, though."

The big boy finished emptying his canoe and waved to Barty and his Dad. Then he got back into it and the three of them paddled off up stream. Their jackets and helmets made them look like strange hump-backed water creatures afloat on the current.

When Barty got home, he took out his journal.

His Mum had bought him some beautiful coloured pencils and a shiny new pencil sharpener. After tea, he tried to draw the dipper, the ducks and the kingfisher.

"Dad, I can't get it right," wailed Barty.

"I'll see if I can get a bird book from the library van when it comes on Thursday," said Dad. "You can copy them from a book."

Barty tried to draw the boys in the canoes, but that was difficult, too. He wrote down what Tom had said about the salmon coming up from the sea, and how it had leapt out of the water. He wrote about the dipper, and how it liked clean, fast-flowing rivers. Mum looked over his shoulder.

"It looks as if you had a good day," she said.

"Oh, yes," breathed Barty.

"Well, now you can enjoy a bath and your bed," said Mum. "You never know, tomorrow might be even better."

6

A Canoe Slalom

Tom Cowden called at the Dobbs' house on his way back from his night-shift at the power station.

"Where's Barty?" he asked, when Mrs Dobbs answered the door.

"Out the back with his Dad," she replied.

"I just called to tell you there's a big canoe competition up the river a bit," said Tom, as he walked out into the back yard. "I thought Barty might like to go and watch."

"Can I go, Dad?" asked Barty.

"There are lots of cars and hundreds of people," said Tom. "I don't think he should go alone."

Barty's Dad looked at the old car tyre he and Barty were recycling into a plant pot.

"This can wait," he said, "if you would like to go, Barty."

"The finish is by The Globe pub," said Tom.

"Right," said Dad.

"I'll come up later, when I'm cleaned up," said Tom.

Barty and his Dad walked along the river bank towards The Globe. All the car parks and every bit of grass verge were packed with cars and minibuses, roof racks, big trailers and tents. Hundreds of young people, dressed in old clothes or swimming trunks, with buoyancy jackets and helmets, were trudging to and fro from the river's edge carrying canoes.

28

When he looked out over the river, Barty could see strings stretched over the water from one bank to the other, with pairs of poles hanging down. Canoeists were paddling in and out of the poles, battling against the white water.

"Why do they all wear helmets?" asked Barty.

"If they tip over," replied Dad, "they might hit their heads on the bottom of the river, and without helmets they might knock themselves out and drown."

"Why are they walking up and down with those funny apron things around their middles?" demanded Barty.

Dad looked around. "Do you see those boys and girls over there, getting into their canoes?" He pointed to a group of canoes on the bank. "Look! See how the apron fits over the cockpit where they sit. It looks as if it keeps the water out."

"Oh," said Barty. He still thought they looked very funny with their long wet legs and flapping aprons, but the competitors didn't seem to care.

Dad lifted Barty up onto his shoulders. From high up, Barty could see the start and the finish of the races. One canoeist at a time went through the poles, and each was timed with a stop watch. Barty found out that the poles were called 'gates'. The crowds on the bank all seemed to be related to someone on the water, or they were teachers with school teams. They yelled encouragement as the canoes swept down the white water, and battled back upstream. It was very exciting.

Scrambling up the bank with a long canoe on his shoulder came a tall thin boy of about sixteen.

"Hello," he said, looking up at Barty on his Dad's shoulder. "Didn't I see you fishing the other day?"

"Was it you who stopped to tip the water out of your canoe?" asked Dad.

"That's me. I went for a swim by mistake. We were practising for this weekend."

"What is it called, this sort of competition?" asked Barty's Dad. "I've often seen those poles strung up there."

"It's called slalom racing," replied the boy. "Our club is the host team. There are clubs and schools from all over the Midlands here today."

"I can see that," said Dad.

"They're camping out overnight," explained the boy. "There are more races tomorrow. My name is Dan, by the way. Dan Warren."

"Hello, Dan," said Dad politely. "I'm Ted Dobbs. This is my son, Bartholomew."

"Whew! That's a long name for a short boy," laughed Dan.

"I'm Barty. Everyone calls me Barty," Barty said.

"Do you live by the river, Barty Dobbs?" asked Dan.

"Yes. Not far from the salmon pool," replied Barty.

"Then you should join our canoe club," said Dan. "It's great."

"Isn't he too small?" asked Dad.

"Not a bit, as long as he can swim. Not all our members are as big as me. We have juniors who are as young as eight years old," said Dan.

"I'm nearly ten," said Barty. "I know I don't look ten, but I am, and I'm tough, really I am."

"Oh yes, he's tough all right," said Dad. "He got his Bronze Survival Badge this term at school."

"That's good," said Dan. "But we don't take new juniors onto the river straight away. They learn to handle the canoe in the swimming pool first. We teach them how to roll and how to fall in and how to get out of the canoe safely before they have a gentle river trip."

"Can I join, Dad, please... please?" begged Barty.

"Well, I don't know. How much does it all cost? I mean, these canoes can't be cheap, and all that special equipment—well—" Dad looked worried.

"You don't have to worry about that," said Dan. "Barty just needs 30p to get into the swimming pool, and we can lend him everything he needs."

"Which day do you teach them?" asked Dad.

"In the school holidays we run a pool training session every day for an hour," said Dan. "Just turn up when you can, at ten o'clock in the morning."

Dan walked off carrying his canoe on his shoulder, with the funny apron thing flapping round his knees.

"Please, Dad, let me learn canoeing," coaxed Barty. "Please."

"We'll have to ask your Mum first," replied Dad, "and check how much money is in the piggy-bank."

Barty stopped pleading. He knew things were difficult because his Dad was out of work. Just then, Tom Cowden came along the river bank.

"Shall we have a pint at The Globe?" he asked. Dad felt in his pockets. "My treat," said Tom. Dad put Barty on the ground.

"Oh, my aching back," he said. "You may be small, our Barty, but you weigh a ton after a while."

Tom went into The Globe and came out with two

glasses of beer and some lemonade on a tray. They sat together on seats in the garden. All around were wet canoeists, their parents and friends. The landlady was doing a brisk trade in cheese rolls, hot dogs and hamburgers. The young people seemed to be forever hungry.

"It must be all that water and fresh air," remarked Tom.

Dad told him all about Dan's idea that Barty should join the Canoe Club. He explained that Barty could borrow all the equipment, so his only problem was getting into town to the swimming pool. Tom thought it was a very good idea.

"They seem very nice young people," he said, "and if they look after the youngsters carefully, I think it'll do Barty good."

Barty and his Dad walked home for lunch. The activity on the river slackened off as the campers settled down at their stoves to cook something, or went to The Globe for more hot dogs and pop. Barty told his mother about the slalom, but wisely left it to his Dad to tell her about learning to paddle a canoe. Mum seemed very worried about it. She thought Barty was too small and would never manage.

"He won't know until he tries," said Dad. "Anyway, he hasn't got many young friends. I think he should go."

"Well, he's not walking into town," snapped Mum.

"That's all right," said Dad. "We go into town on Thursday anyway, to get the shopping. We'll leave Barty at the pool and fetch him at eleven o'clock.

That'll give him one day to try it out. After that...
well... we'll have to see."

With that, Mum and Barty had to be content.
Mum couldn't argue about Barty trying something
once, and Barty had to agree to wait until Thursday
when his Dad could take him to the swimming pool
in the van.

They watched more of the slalom races on the
Sunday. At the prize-giving, a canoe club from
Worcester was first, but one of the local girls won an
individual prize in her group. Dan was about halfway
down his group. But he didn't mind. He hadn't been
canoeing long himself. He said he was glad that
Barty was going to the pool on Thursday, and went
off to help with the clearing up.

Dad realized that there was a lot of work to be
done clearing the campsite, picking up litter, sorting
lost property and so on. He and Barty offered to
help, and stayed a long time, working with the other
helpers. The landlady at The Globe came out with
beer or cider for the grown-ups and pop for the
younger ones, and lots of sausage rolls for supper.

When Barty and his Dad got home very late,
Mum was really angry. "You might have let me
know," she said. "I've been thinking the worst! And
fancy letting Barty drink pop at this time of night.
You know what will happen!"

It did. A combination of pop and lively dreams
about canoes and weirs meant that Barty woke up
soaking wet. He cried as he stripped his bed, because
he was so angry with himself. Now Mum wouldn't
let him join the Canoe Club. He was sure she
wouldn't.

Surprisingly his Mum was quite calm. "You've

33

been very much better for weeks," she said. "Don't worry, Barty. It was just the exciting day you had."

Barty still felt angry with himself. He stayed indoors to write about the canoe slalom in his journal. He had been so happy watching it, and had felt like a normal boy. Now he was back to feeling like a silly little dwarf. No one was ever as angry with Barty as he was with himself!

He felt better as he drew his pictures, colouring them carefully. He thought about Thursday. In the morning he was going to the swimming pool, and in the afternoon the library van would bring him a picture book of birds.

7

Pool Training

Waiting for Thursday to come, Barty and his Dad worked on the allotment and finished off the car-tyre plant pots. Amanda came back from the school camping trip full of airs and graces, but she didn't speak to Barty and he didn't ask her about the camp. One evening they went fishing and Barty watched a heron catch his supper.

The council mowers came and cut the grass verges round the lanes, so the riot of poppies and cow parsley disappeared. Dad said it was safer for car drivers, but it didn't look so pretty. The river level dropped lower still, as there had been no rain for a fortnight. Tom said if it didn't rain soon, the last of the salmon would be walking up river, not swimming.

On Wednesday night it started to rain. It was still raining on Thursday. When Barty woke up he felt sad. He had really been enjoying the hot sunny days by the river. Then he cheered up. It was Thursday and he was going to find out how to paddle a canoe.

He scrambled out of his bed and searched for his swimming trunks. They were right at the bottom of the airing cupboard, so it took him a long time to put back the towels and sheets he had moved. They still didn't look right when he had finished.

Mum was at the kitchen table writing her shopping list. She checked with Dad on how the vegetables were coming on. At the allotment they had potatoes, baby carrots, peas, lettuce, radishes, spring onions and some beans. The strawberries were finished, but the rows of raspberry canes were producing fruit. Mum listened carefully to Dad and scribbled on her piece of paper. She tried not to waste money when she went shopping, and only allowed one or two treats a week, depending on the special offers at the supermarket—Barty didn't get too many sweets and crisps. The dentist was pleased, even if Barty wasn't. He hoped that today the supermarket would be giving a special price on large bars of fruit-and-nut chocolate, his favourite.

Mum's list was ready, the van was at the front door and Barty stood ready with his duffle-bag over his shoulder. He sat patiently through his Mum's stream of advice and warnings. She kept it up all the way to the town, and then on the walk from the car park to the cash desk at the swimming pool.

"Oh dear," she concluded. "I'm sure we shouldn't leave him here on his own."

"He won't be on his own," said Dad quietly. "It *is* a training session for children, so there will be lots of others around."

"Oh, you know what I mean."

The trouble was, of course, that Barty's Mum was worried about his being teased, or frightened, or getting too tired, or just hating it.

"Mum, I'm nearly ten. Lots of ten-year-olds go to the pool by themselves," said Barty.

"He'll be all right," said the lady at the cash desk. "They're well looked after." She smiled down at Barty as she gave him a ticket, and he shot into the

36

dressing rooms before his Mum could say another word.

"See you at eleven o'clock," called Dad as he dragged Mum off to the shops.

Barty knew his way round the swimming pool because his primary school used it once a week for their swimming and survival lessons. Barty's teachers were surprised at how quickly he had learned to swim. He seemed very strong across the shoulders. Now he would find out if his strong arms and shoulders were useful in a canoe.

As he left the changing room, he saw that the pool was roped off into two sections. At the deep end some teenagers were rolling over and righting their canoes. It looked very easy. They were not wearing the fat buoyancy aids that they used on the river and looked quite normal.

At the shallow end, in short round-ended canoes, were a number of junior beginners. Standing in the water beside each junior was a senior club member or a parent from the Canoe Club. Watching from the gallery were more parents and friends.

Barty walked to the water's edge, his confidence oozing away. Children stared at him. Some giggled and pointed. Luckily one or two were from his own school, and knew him slightly. They waved to him. Some of the helpers in the water looked very surprised to see him. Just then the pool manager came over.

"Hello, Philip," he said.

"I'm Barty," replied Barty, giggling. It was the pool manager's habit to call all boys 'Philip' and all girls 'Phyllis'. He said he saw thousands of kids every week, and could never remember all their names.

"That's right, Philip," said the pool manager. "Joining the Canoe Club?"

"Yes," replied Barty, smiling. "A boy called Dan invited me."

"Oh, Dan!" said the pool manager. He knew Dan all right, even if he did pretend all the boys were called Philip. "Danny! Customer for you!" he yelled.

One of the deep-end rollers climbed out of the pool and walked up to them. Barty recognized Dan. He looked bigger than ever. He was nearly six feet tall—Barty was about half his height.

"What a team," laughed the pool manager.

Dan found a spare small canoe. He tried to adjust the foot-rest to suit Barty's rather short legs but it was difficult. The pool manager brought them one of the polystyrene floats that was normally used for swimming lessons. It did just the trick, giving Barty something to brace his legs against. Soon he was afloat with the other children. Dan pushed him around for a bit, just to get him used to floating on the water. Then he passed Barty a paddle, the shortest there was. It was a ridiculous-looking thing, far too big, and Barty didn't know how to hold it. If Dan had not been wading in the water beside him, Barty would have been very frightened. Dan spoke quietly and showed him how to dip and turn the paddle, not dipping too deep and not splashing too much. Barty floundered and puffed, wobbling everywhere. All around him, confident eight year olds were happily paddling their canoes. Barty felt tired and flustered.

"Keep calm. It isn't the Olympic Games," said Dan. "That's right. Nice and steady." Suddenly the splashing stopped. The roof of the pool stayed still, in its proper place, and Barty paddled smoothly across the width of the pool. It wasn't a fluke. He paddled back just as well to the other side. Red-faced with effort and pride, he smiled at Dan.

"Great! That's fine," cheered Dan.

"Can I roll now?" asked Barty.

"Steady on," replied Dan. "Let's paddle round a bit now." Dan dog-paddled behind as Barty took his canoe all round the shallow end. To his great pleasure, the canoe began to go exactly where he wanted it to go. He felt his breathing get easier, and his face cooled down. A loud whistle blew.

"Out of it, you lot," yelled the pool manager. "Let's get the paying public in!" He always yelled and sounded bossy, but he could be very kind and patient. He coaxed nervous children into swimming with confidence, and taught the wilder boys how to dive properly. When they had learned how to do that they seemed to behave too, instead of pushing and splashing. He also coached promising swimmers for competitions, always in his bossy barking voice. The children quickly learned to obey the rules at the pool, and to like the man who made them.

"Well, Philip, get going then!" barked the pool manager.

"Yes," said Barty.

"Well, don't just stand there dripping. Go to the loo and get dressed," he yelled. He knew about Barty's problems from the primary school, but he never went on about them.

Barty grinned at him and plodded off. Dan stayed to put the canoes in the racks and then followed Barty into the dressing room.

"Coming again tomorrow?" asked Dan.

"I'm not sure," said Barty. "I don't know if Dad will bring me."

He dried himself carefully. He knew his Mum would go on at him if he didn't. He felt a bit shivery and his chest ached.

"There's a hot drink machine," said Dan. "I'd have a hot drink if I were you."

"I spent all my money to get in," said Barty. "I didn't know about drinks."

"I'll treat you today," offered Dan. "You can treat me another day."

When Mum and Dad arrived to collect Barty, they found him with a group of young people, sipping hot chocolate and laughing as some of them told of their adventures on, or in, the river with their canoes.

"See," whispered Dad, "he's just one of the crowd. Now mind you don't fuss over him."

Mum swallowed the words she had been about to say. "Hello," she smiled.

Barty beamed at her. "These are all in the Canoe Club," he said, waving his arm around.

Mum and Dad smiled at them. Dad felt he'd end up like Mr Whitley, the pool manager, calling them all Philip or Phyllis, if he had to learn all their names.

"See you tomorrow, Barty," they all called.

"Oh, I don't know," said Mum.

"He'll be here," said Dad firmly, taking Mum's arm in his.

"Goodbye, everybody," called Barty happily, a chocolate moustache round his mouth.

"Now what did you say that for?" demanded Mum when they were outside in the car park. "How is he going to get here?"

"Because I'll cut down on smoking and I won't go to the pub. So the money can be spent on petrol to take Barty to the pool. Now we'll say no more about it," said Dad.

In fact, after a few days of training, a lady came up and spoke to Dad at the pool.

"Hello, I'm Mrs Greyson," she said. "I live in Lower Crossleigh, so I come through your village every day with my two. Shall I pick Barty up on my way?"

Dad was embarrassed, but grateful. "Can't we take it in turns?" he asked.

"My two are absolute demons," she said. "I wouldn't inflict them on anyone. Still... perhaps sometimes... yes, I'd be glad for you to bring them in." So Barty had a regular lift with the Terrible Twins, aged twelve, for the rest of the pool training sessions. Dad's pride was soothed, as two or three times Mrs Greyson let the twins pile into his old van. They regarded this as a treat, espcially as Barty's Mum gave them home-made biscuits.

"You are small, aren't you?" said Eddie on the first lift. "A proper titch!"

"Yes, I am," replied Barty, "but I'm tough, so watch it!"

"Well done," laughed Elaine, the other twin. "See, Eddie, he may be small but he won't be bullied by someone like you."

8

The Hide

When the library van came and parked in the village it brought Barty two lovely books, one on birds and one on trees and flowers. The librarian gave Barty a third book, too, a very thin one, with lots of photographs.

"That booklet was written by one of my friends at the library," she said. "It took him nearly two years to do it. He took all the photographs himself. They show all the wild life round here. It's a conservation area, you know."

Barty looked through the little book. He recognized some of the places, and some of the creatures in the photographs.

"You can keep it if you like," said the librarian. Barty was very pleased. He put his books carefully in his carrier bag, along with his mother's novels and his father's gardening books.

"Having a rotten holiday?" came a hated voice.

"Oh, hello, Amanda," said Barty.

"I'm just going on my *second* holiday," boasted Amanda. "I bet you've got nothing at all in your journal yet."

"Not much," said Barty. The librarian winked at him as he went down the steps of the van. She had heard all about the journals and she knew how hard Barty was working on his.

Barty's Mum, returning one day from a long

walk, had come in with her old camera loaded with film. The chemist at the shop in town had looked it over and said that it would still work, so Mum had bought a colour film for it. She thought Barty could take some colour photographs to put in his journal. He had already used some of the film to take pictures of Dan and the others in their canoes, and one of Tom with his fishing rod and basket. He had even taken one of his Mum and Dad on the allotment. Now, looking at the booklet the librarian had given him, he wanted to photograph the birds on the riverside for himself.

He and Dad chatted about it as they sat in the back yard munching warm scones with strawberry jam.

"How did that library man get so close to the birds and things?" asked Barty. "Every time I go to look at a water rat or moorhens, they just swim off. What did he do?"

"I reckon he hid for hours," said Dad. "He must have had a little hut or something, and got up very early and hidden in it all day, not just once but lots of times."

"Could I hide?" asked Barty.

"I think he had a better camera than that one," said Dad. "Still, you could try. The swans keep fairly still. Try to get a picture of a swan with its cygnets first."

"Now?" asked Barty.

"Tomorrow," said Dad.

Tom Cowden was very interested in the idea of making a little hide, so he helped as well, bringing some old sacks along. They found a spot not too far from the salmon pool, and made Barty a really tiny hide. They put branches over the sacks but left a small window so Barty could watch the birds. He thought that even if he never photographed anything, it was the best hide a boy could ever have. He wouldn't tell anyone about it.

He didn't need the hide to photograph the swans. The cob and the pen (Tom told him that was what the male and female swans were called), came gliding gracefully down the river, followed by their brown-coloured cygnets. The cob held his wings up high, ready to protect his family. Barty took a snapshot with his camera, and got two or three good shots.

He seemed to be very busy. What with gardening, fishing, taking photographs, canoe training and writing his journal, he didn't have time to be bored. He was very pleased and excited about his progress in canoeing. Dan seemed to think he was doing well, and the grown-ups at the club were surprised at the strength he had in his arms and shoulders. Once in the water, there seemed to be little difference between Barty and the other children who were beginners like him.

Mr Whitley, the pool manager, had quite taken to the tiny boy and sometimes, if Barty was waiting for a turn in a canoe, he helped him to improve his swimming style. He showed him how to smooth out the splashes and get the most power from his arms, so that Barty could feel how much easier it was to get through the water. He began to have much more confidence, both in the canoe and in the water. Mr Whitley started to call him Tom instead of Philip. When Barty asked him why, he laughed. "Get your Mum to read *The Water Babies* to you," he said.

The Canoe Club juniors began to accept him. At

first they made a bit of a pet of him. That felt worse to Barty than when they had laughed at him or been unkind. It made him angry to be fussed over or treated as a special case. Only his Mum was allowed to do that. When he proved that he was as good as them, and took part in splash fights and duckings with good humour, they began to treat him as one of the crowd. Barty felt very proud about that.

After just over two weeks of training in the pool every day, Barty heard about the river trip. The club seniors were going to take the junior beginners for a trip down river on Sunday. When Dad came to fetch Barty (it was his turn to drive), Eddie and Elaine were full of it.

"We're driving to that farm by the big bend in the river, and then paddling back to the Canoe Club hut. The canoes are being taken to the starting point on trailers," said Eddie.

"It takes hours," said Elaine, "but there are no rapids or anything. It isn't dangerous."

"Is Barty coming?" asked Eddie. Barty wanted to go more than anything, but he didn't dare ask. Dan came out of the changing rooms with John, the organizer.

"Hello, Mr Dobbs," said Dan. "Is Barty coming on Sunday?"

"We've got a canoe and buoyancy aid for him, all the right size," said John. "He can have a lift to the start."

"Oh, I don't know... er... " murmured Dad.

"He can come in our car," said Dan. "My Mum is driving me to the start at Parsloe's Farm, and then picking me up at the Canoe Club afterwards. She's doing tea and things for everyone at the finish."

John saw that Mr Dobbs still looked very worried. "We have three Indian canoes—doubles—that we use as rescue boats. There is a senior in each," he said. "If a junior gets very tired or capsizes, they can come in a double with us, while someone else takes over their canoe."

"Besides," said Dan, "he's a better canoeist than me. Let him come. He only needs a packed lunch and some spare clothes."

"Go on, Mr Dobbs, let him come. It'll be great," pleaded Eddie.

Barty had said not one word, and yet Dad found himself promising to let him go on a four-hour trip down the river. He dreaded to think what Mum would say.

"See you at half-past eight on Sunday," said Dan. "My Mum will call for you."

"Four hours in a canoe?" cried Mum, when Dad tried to tell her about the river trip. "Our Barty? Four hours! You're both quite mad. Whatever made you say he could go? Can I phone Dan's mother? She mustn't waste her time coming here. Oh dear!" Mrs Dobbs was really frightened at the idea. She went on the whole evening until after Barty's bedtime, raising every objection she could think of. Dad muttered soothing comments at intervals.

The next day she was a bit calmer. Tom Cowden called in. He said that if the Canoe Club organizers thought that Barty was up to the trip and would be safe, then he would be.

"They take special training, these instructors," he said. "And look how they've taught Barty so far and taken care of him. You've got to let him go on the river sometime. Why not this Sunday?"

Gradually Mum came round. It was, after all, the school holidays. She could keep Barty in bed all the next day if he got overtired. She still felt worried, though, and cheered herself up by having a big cooking session. If Dan's mother was going to make teas for everyone at the end of the trip, then Mrs Dobbs was going to make a lot of cakes and scones for them all to eat. Barty laughed to himself. All the problems in the world could be solved by a good baking session, according to his Mum.

9

Down the River

Barty didn't go to the swimming pool on Saturdays, so he decided to use his hide. His Mum and Dad knew exactly where he was, and he promised not to wander, so they let him go alone.

He settled in his hide with the camera, the bird book from the library, some crayons and some of his Mum's shelf paper. He had learned very quickly that it was best to practise a drawing first before putting it into the journal. If there was nothing to photograph he could pass the time drawing.

The kingfisher still didn't pause by the hide to eat his minnows, but Barty saw the swan family again, some mallard ducks, coots and moorhens. He knew what they were but looked them up in his bird book all the same, and then settled down to watch for something else. He saw a long piece of silvery weed wriggling in the water. Then he thought, no, that isn't weed. It was the biggest fish he had ever seen. Its head pointed upstream and its tail moved slowly, just keeping it steady in the deeper water. It was dark on top and silvery underneath, with rosy red around the gills. Barty was fascinated. He tried to guess how long it was, and how heavy, but because of the movement of the water he found this too difficult. The fish swam against the current, moving slowly up river. It came to the shallow water rushing over the rocks, gathered its strength, and leapt right over, landing in the deeper water on the other side with a big silvery splash. The ripples spread across the river, wider and wider, but the giant of the river was gone. Barty hoped no one would catch it further up the river. Tom Cowden would be interested to hear about it, though.

Sunday came and the Dobbs family were up very early. The sky looked cloudy and threatened rain.

"Don't worry. We'll get wet anyway," said Barty to his anxious mother.

She buttered the scones and put them and all the cakes she had made into a basket covered with a clean tea-towel. Barty had his spare dry clothes in a thick dustbin bag sealed with sticky tape. He was wearing his swimming trunks under very old jeans, with a torn T-shirt and an outgrown cagoule on top. He thought he would get much too hot but Mum had insisted.

A car horn sounded outside. It was Dan's mother in her little car. Dan had tied his canoe to the roof rack with stretchy cables. He was walking up to the front door but Barty opened it before he had time to knock—and Mum was close behind him.

"It's ever so good of you to take him," she began, "and I hope he'll be all right. He—"

"He'll be quite safe," said Dan cheerfully. "Please don't worry, Mrs Dobbs. I'll look after him for you, and it isn't like a slalom."

Mrs Dobbs hadn't seen the slalom races, so she didn't know what Dan meant, but Barty did. He aimed a kick at Dan's ankles.

"Ssssh!" he said. "Don't describe a slalom to her, please, or she'll never let me on the river."

"Here are some things for the tea afterwards,"

said Barty's Mum to Dan's mother through the car window.

"That's kind of you," said Dan's mother, as Dan put the basket and Barty's dry clothing in the boot of the car.

"Well, it's the least I can do to thank you for giving our Barty a lift," replied Mrs Dobbs.

Barty climbed into the back seat of the car looking really scruffy. His Mum almost felt ashamed of him, but Dan looked just as bad. She was feeling very uneasy. Usually if Barty went out, she took care to make him look really nice. This outdoor life her little boy seemed to be set on, with his tall friends and their scruffy clothes, would take some getting used to. Dad seemed to understand. He gave her a big hug.

"He'll be all right, you know. And it's a good thing to let him go with a crowd of youngsters. Really."

"I know," gulped Mum, smoothing her apron, "but he, he... Here! Did you notice that Dan's mother? She'd got old jeans on, just like a girl, and she must be as old as me. Fancy!"

Dad laughed. If his wife was noticing what someone else was wearing, then she wasn't worrying too much about Barty.

Dan's mother drove very carefully. She said that the wind made the car behave badly when she had the canoe on the roof. She didn't say too much as they drove along to Parsloe's Farm. When they got there, they saw lots of other cars in the farmyard with roof-racks loaded with canoes. There was also a minibus towing a trailer full of canoes. Some of these were the small, round-ended training canoes, but there were also some general purpose canoes with pointed ends, deeper than the slalom canoes, with room for dry clothes and a picnic.

The juniors were excitedly sorting out the helmets and life-jackets, while their parents stood around, some looking rather anxious and others very proud. Some were looking up at the sky, where the clouds loomed blacker than ever.

"Where will you picnic?" asked Mrs Warren.

"Just beyond the ox-bow," answered Dan.

"I'll see you at about half-past three, then," she said, as Dan lifted the canoe off the roof-rack.

"Cheerio!" called Dan as she drove off. "Now, let's find your canoe, Barty."

John was there, and Neil, Adrian, another John, Chris, Terry, Elaine, Eddie, Anne, Paula, Sue... so many of his friends to say hello to. They found Barty's canoe by the trailer. It was a junior-sized all-purpose canoe, with a paddle about two feet taller than Barty. He took a helmet from the pile and adjusted it to fit. He then put on a bright orange buoyancy aid over all the other clothes his mother had made him wear. This would keep his head above water if he fell out of the canoe and hit his head on the rocks.

The canoes had to be carried from the farmyard down to the water. Everyone carried their own, including Barty. He didn't want any favours, so he hitched his canoe onto one shoulder and plodded off, following the others. The path was a cattle track, and rather muddy. Barty was glad he had on his really old trainers to walk to the launching place— Mum would have a fit if she could see the state of the track. The launching place was a broad sort of beach where the cows waded in to drink, and it was quite bare of grass. On the opposite bank were some fishermen watching the arrival of the Canoe Club curiously and with some apprehension.

Barty heard the other mothers and fathers issuing instructions to the juniors. They seemed every bit as worried as his own mother, and that cheered him up. The river looked very deep and calm here, with dark green weed at the bottom. It felt cold to their hands as they pushed their canoes in, and sat inside them to fit the spray-decks. Barty had learned that this was what the funny aprons were called.

Two seniors set off first. Two other senior girls were paddling a two-man Indian canoe, and a father and teenage son took another. Barty noticed that every junior had a senior close by, so that none of the beginners was left to struggle or feel nervous. Dan was his particular friend and paddled only a few yards away from him.

With more confidence than he really felt, Barty set off. It was so different from the swimming pool. In spite of looking deep and still, the river flowed quite fast. Luckily, they were travelling downstream, so that even if he just floated, he would still find himself going the right way. He tried paddling with the long paddle. The weeks of pool training paid off. It was hard work, but he could do it. He kept his place in the line of canoes, paddling strongly and going where he wanted to go. Down the river went this large party of brightly-coloured ducklings, shepherded by their 'two-man' mother ducks. The fishermen waved to them and called, 'Good Luck!'

As they continued, Barty's confidence grew and he began to look around him. They were paddling past fields where black and white cows grazed. The grass looked brownish. It needed rain, but Barty hoped the rain would keep off until they were home. He could see the distant hills, blue and misty. Across the farthest field was the road home, with cars rushing along it. The group were paddling quite fast, but it would take them a long time, compared with the cars. Barty thought he would rather be in his canoe than in a Rolls Royce just then.

He was surprised at how the river changed. If he had ever thought about it before, he would have imagined that it stayed much the same as it was by his house all the way to the sea. But here it broadened out into a wide, shallow, slow-moving stream, curving round a big bend, with flat meadows on both sides. Dan said that the meadows flooded when the river rose after heavy rain.

"One day," he said, "the river will take a short cut across the field instead of flowing round it."

"When?" asked Barty.

"Oh, in thousands of years, I expect," laughed Dan. "We learned that in geography at school."

One farmer had some Canada geese on his stretch of water and pure white ducks, which quacked and swam away as the canoes came near them. The group was more spread out now. Some juniors, in a full-sized canoe for the first time, had turned upside down but soon righted themselves without getting upset. Nobody had needed the rescue canoes so far and it was nearly lunchtime.

After one more big bend in the river, the canoeists came to another farm. Here, the farmer's wife had put up a big table on the bank, with hot drinks for everyone. They landed their canoes, tipped out the water, and got out their lunch bags.

Barty wasn't the first to arrive, but neither was he the last. He hauled his canoe out of the water and undid his polythene dustbin bag. Inside, he found his clean dry clothes—but no packed lunch! His Mum had been so busy packing cakes and scones for the Club tea that she had packed his sandwiches with them. Now his lunch was at the Canoe Club hut.

Tears filled his eyes. He felt so silly. Everyone was unpacking waterproof boxes and bags, swapping sandwiches and other goodies. The farmer's wife looked at the tiny boy with the tears running down his face.

"What's up?" she demanded. "Did your lunch fall in the river?"

"No," replied Barty. "I just haven't got any lunch—not a scrap." He explained what had happened, about his Mum and her cooking and everything.

"Hey, you lot," she shouted to the others. "There's a little river monster here who's starving to death. He needs at least four sandwiches to keep him quiet."

The others heard the sad tale, and everyone offered him something. He had more sandwiches and cakes than he could possibly eat, and nobody laughed at him at all. Dan gave him a peanut and banana sandwich, something his Mum would never approve of. Sue gave him tuna and cress, Eddie shared his egg, and someone else offered him ham. There were also jam tarts, biscuits, and cake. Barty cheered up and tucked in with the rest. One small girl really *had* lost her sandwiches in the bottom of the river, and one of the adults in charge had forgotten about the picnic altogether, so Barty stopped feeling silly quite soon.

At that moment the rain, which had been threatening all morning, started to pour down. The hot drinks were diluted with rain, the table was soaked and the sandwiches grew soggy. The canoeists started to become a bit chilly. While they had been paddling, the water didn't make them cold, but sitting on a bank in the rain made everyone shiver. They cleared up the litter, said goodbye to the friendly farmer's wife and set off again. The exercise warmed them up and the helmets kept the rain out of their eyes, but it was less fun now, and they just worked hard to get home as soon as they could.

Barty paddled until his shoulders ached, his back ached and his neck ached. The girls in the double Indian canoe came up and asked if he wanted a rest, but Barty would not give in. He paddled on with Dan close by. Dan could have gone faster but he didn't want his small friend to be left alone. He did his best to encourage Barty and watched him carefully. Barty's face had a set expression. He was not going to let Dan down.

The river began to narrow. It ran between steeply-wooded banks, and the bottom was rocky. There was some white water where the river rushed over the rocks. Barty gulped. He had never canoed over white water. You didn't get that in a swimming pool. Dan went first, showing Barty how to let the water carry him safely without doing more than steer with the paddle. Then it was Barty's turn. He felt his canoe snatched by the angry water. It turned sideways of its own accord. Barty steered with his paddle as Dan had done and the canoe suddenly dropped. He was scared. He thought the paddle would spin away and he would go under.

Then he bobbed gently into calmer water alongside Dan's canoe. He had made it! He smiled through the rain at Dan, and they paddled on. They were nearly home. The other seniors guided their juniors through the rapids and no one capsized. The juniors began to feel like seasoned voyagers. They were all safely on the last lap of the journey.

Barty barely remembered the last lap of the river trip. He arrived at the club hut feeling so tired that he could hardly walk when they landed. Lots of other juniors were feeling the same.

The canoes had to be lifted out of the water and put on their racks. For once he did not let his pride prevent him from accepting offers of help, and someone's dad put his canoe away for him. He put on his dry, neat clothes and climbed into the back of Mrs Warren's car. He missed out on tea completely, for he fell asleep and slept until Mrs Warren dropped him off at home. Then he went straight up the stairs and fell into bed.

His mother had to wait until the next day to hear all the details of his adventure. Despite dreaming about the river and the white water and the pouring rain, his bed was quite dry in the morning. And it was a very proud, but extremely stiff, Barty who entertained his Mum and Dad with an account of all his adventures.

10

Barty's Fight

For a few days after the river trip, Barty was content to stay quietly at home. His muscles ached for some time, but he was delighted that they seemed to be harder after all his training. Mum said he looked really brown and healthy this summer, but she was pleased that he had decided to have a few days' rest.

He spent some time in the back garden, writing and drawing in his journal. Mum had his photographs printed at the chemist's, and he stuck them in the journal next to the appropriate pages of writing. The best pictures were the ones of the swan family. The reflection in the water was so clear that it looked like another swan family upside down.

He enjoyed using the coloured pencils. They seemed to make a nicer picture and more natural colours than felt-tipped pens. He tried to draw a map of the Canoe Club's journey down the river, but he found it very hard. He marked the places where he had seen the geese, and the farm where they had eaten their lunch. He drew squiggly patterns to show where he had gone through the rapids for the first time. He was pleased that he had nearly filled his journal—it was beginning to look quite old and well used now.

He didn't go to any more pool training sessions. A new batch of beginners had started, and Barty's group did all their canoeing on the river by the club hut now. There was a long waiting list to join the Canoe Club, Barty discovered. He had been allowed to join because Dan had asked specially. For once Barty was glad he had been treated as a special case. If he had gone on the waiting list he wouldn't have made so many friends or learned to paddle a canoe. Dan was a real friend.

★ ★ ★

The Canoe Club met on Wednesday evenings and Sunday mornings as well as other times when the boys on holiday from school could get a group together. There was some white water right by the club hut and Barty's group of juniors learned to go up and down river by using the current, and also to go across it, which was much more difficult! Sometimes they put the slalom poles out for a practice. Once Barty decided he wanted to have a go at the slalom. He paddled off bravely but tipped his canoe over straight away. He came to the surface quickly enough, spluttering and gasping, but only to see his canoe and paddle rapidly drifting away. If it hadn't been for the prompt action of the older boys he would have lost both of them and perhaps been swept away himself as the river flowed particularly fast there. But with a loud cry of 'swimmer' from the watcher, a swift rescue was carried out. Barty then understood the very strict rules about never canoeing alone—there must always be at least three on the water and three watching on the bank.

After the rain that nearly spoiled the river trip, the weather grew warm again, with plenty of sunshine. The river level dropped, revealing huge slabs of rock in the shallows. The Canoe Club committee decided that the hut and nearby car park badly needed repairing, weeding and redecorating, and everyone was asked to help.

Barty came home with a typed letter from the Club Secretary. It invited all Canoe Club members and their parents to bring tools and other equipment for working on the hut and car park, and also some food for a barbecue afterwards. Mum said she would be glad to make some food for the barbecue, and Dad said that one thing he had plenty of was time to help mend things. Dad went out to the shed to sort out which tools would be most useful. He would need paintbrushes, scrapers, a screwdriver and a hammer. He would take his scythe to cut down the stinging nettles and other tall weeds. He also found some paint left over from decorating the house, which he thought might be useful.

Barty's Mum did her shopping on Wednesday instead of Thursday. She bought some fresh minced beef to make her own hamburgers. She said you got more for your money that way, and you knew what all the ingredients were. She baked sausage rolls and ginger parkin with treacle. Barty told her that she didn't have to try and feed the whole Canoe Club all by herself, but she chased him out of the kitchen.

Dad was loading tools into the van, humming to himself. He looked just as he used to when he went to work every day, rather busy and serious, but happy. Barty tried to help but his Dad told him to leave the tools alone. Barty wandered off to the allotment. The strawberries and raspberries were all finished. He sat on an upturned bucket popping peapods to eat the baby peas inside. Some of the pods had wriggly maggots.

Maggots made him think of fishing. With Mum and Dad so busy, he thought he would get his rod and go to the river to look at his hide and try to catch a fish. He hadn't any maggots except the tiny ones from the pea-pods, so he dug in the compost heap for worms.

It was cool by the river. Tom Cowden was at work, but there were some strangers fishing by the peg that Tom liked best, who had driven their car out from the city. The wives sat knitting in camp chairs, chatting quietly as the men set up their rods. Barty plodded past them. The women paused in their knitting. They stared hard at Barty with 'That Look' on their faces.

"Go home, little boy. You shouldn't be here by yourself," shouted one woman.

"Ought to have more sense than to let a child like that out," muttered the other. "What are his parents thinking of?"

"Glad mine are normal," remarked the first woman.

Barty walked on, making no reply. He had almost forgotten 'That Look' during this busy holiday. His ears went hot and red. He shivered as if the sun had gone in. When he reached his hide, he found two pasty-faced boys playing in it.

"Hey!" called Barty. "That's my hide."

"Not now it isn't," said the bigger of the two boys, who was about twelve, freckled and fat.

"It's our place," said the younger boy, aged about ten, but still, of course, much bigger than Barty.

"It's mine. My Dad made it for me," said Barty.

"Who's your Dad, then? King of the goblins?" laughed the older boy.

"Ha! Ha! It's a river dwarf," screamed the younger one, jumping up and down. "It's a troll. Yuk!"

Barty saw red. Six weeks ago he would have cried and run home. Now, with the thought of all his new friends, who didn't seem to notice his size and shape, he decided he wasn't going to be called names any more—not by summer tourists, anyway. He rushed at the city boys, dropping his bag and fishing rod as he charged like an angry little bull. He butted one with his head, but the other boy grabbed his legs. They all rolled over on the ground, squashing Barty's hide flat. Barty kicked and struggled, but it was very hard to fight two boys, even with his hard muscles. The boys grabbed Barty by his arms and legs and in his angry struggle, Barty fell in the river. His clothes felt heavy and his shoes filled up with river water, but he managed to swim downstream a bit, with the boys' cruel laughter ringing in his ears. He climbed out onto the bank and made his way home by a different path.

He heard the two city boys laughing and splashing about and dropping stones in the water until their Dads told them off for disturbing the fish. The two women continued placidly knitting, not in the least disturbed by the episode. They had quite forgotten about Barty. Then the boys found Barty's fishing rod and bag, and decided to go and fish by their fathers.

Barty squelched on home. He felt utterly sick at heart. He had to go up the road with water streaming from his clothes but, for once, nobody was around to stare at him. Mum and Dad were in the kitchen having a well-earned cup of tea. Barty stood in the doorway, dripping onto the mat. Mum let out a shriek, clattering her cup on its saucer.

"Where have you been, you naughty boy?" she demanded.

"I—I—went f—fishing—" stuttered Barty.

"It looks like it," said Dad. He sounded very angry.

"Barty, you know the rules. You never go to the river without telling us."

"You were so busy—" began Barty.

"I could listen, even if my hands were busy, couldn't I?" said Mum.

"I—I suppose so," he mumbled.

"And how did you come to fall in?" demanded Dad grimly.

"It was two boys from the city. They'd got in my hide. We had a fight. They threw me in... sort of... well... I fell—"

"Fighting?" shrieked Mum. "Barty Dobbs, I'm ashamed of you."

Dad and Mum were very angry. Barty had broken their rules made for his own safety, and worse, he had been fighting visitors. The visitors paid for their fishing tickets. They bought things in the village shop. They had meals and drinks in the village pub. Visitors were good for the village, and Barty had been fighting them. Dad asked angrily where the fishing tackle was, and Barty suddenly remembered that he had dropped it at the start of the fight. He burst into tears. His rod had been a Christmas present from Mum and Dad. Mum sent him up to his room, while Dad set off to look for the rod and bag.

Dad found the city families. The boys were fishing quietly enough by their fathers, but Dad noticed that they were using Barty's rod. They said it was their own rod, but Dad pointed to the mark he had made on it for Barty. The two fathers were annoyed but gave the things back. They laughed at the idea of a fight.

"Our boys wouldn't bother fighting a midget," they said. "Our boys are normal, healthy lads, out for a day by the river."

The two mothers told Dad off for letting Barty out. "Fancy letting a deformed child like that wander about spoiling people's pleasure—nasty-tempered creature!"

Dad felt very upset and angry. He felt like telling them a thing or two but in the end he didn't bother. He simply picked up Barty's fishing tackle, checked on the broken hide, and walked away.

Mum was clattering and banging at the kitchen sink—always a bad sign. Dad put Barty's fishing things in the shed.

"He's staying upstairs," said Mum. "No barbecue for him tonight."

"He *was* very naughty," agreed Dad, "but I've just met those people. They... they were not very nice. They made remarks about Barty... They said he shouldn't be allowed out... they suggested that he was... mental... as well. You'd think he was a monster the way they went on... *and* they would have kept his fishing things." Dad paused, too upset to go on. "I—I nearly had a fight myself."

Mum asked some questions and made a few comments, but she was nearly crying.

"I reckon they provoked him all right," said Dad at last.

"Even so," said Mum, "our Barty shouldn't have been there without asking. He was a silly boy."

"Let him come to the barbecue," said Dad. "Honestly, I could have pushed them in the river myself."

"No," said Mum. "He has got to learn his lesson. He went off, he got into a fight with visitors. He got soaking wet. No. He can't go."

"I was really looking forward to working on the club hut," said Dad, sadly.

"*You* can go, can't you?" asked Mum. "You don't have to take Barty with you to go and help them."

"He is the club member. I am his guest," said Dad. "Guests can't just turn up without the member who invited them. It is a shame about all that food."

"We can take the food along. We owe the Canoe Club that at least," said Mum.

"Yes, but I don't see how we can stay and eat it, with Barty at home in bed," said Dad.

Mum looked at him. Dad had a perfectly serious face. He meant it. If Barty did not go and do his share of the work, then none of the Dobbs family could stay for the barbecue. Mum had really been looking forward to it as well. She thought of the hamburgers and the sausage rolls, and the parkin. What a waste it would be if no one could share it all.

"Well," she said, "you go and give him a good talking to, and he can rest until after tea. Then we'll go, but only because he promised to help with the work, mind."

Dad went upstairs. Barty was crying into his pillow. He was very hot and sticky, with red eyes and a runny nose. Dad sat on the bed.

"Go away! The whole holiday is spoiled," cried Barty. "It's all spoiled."

"What is spoiled?" asked Dad quietly.

"I—I—thought I was really getting on well and making friends and—and—those pigs—those kids from the city—well, they call me names, they spoil my hide—but everyone's the same. They all hate me and call me names. It's going to be like this all my life. I'm never going out again—ever."

Dad sat still for a while watching the unhappy little boy. He was angry himself and had to think hard to find the right words.

"A hide is spoiled. That's all," he said.

"And I lost my fishing stuff," sobbed Barty, "The rod and bag and keep-net, my Christmas presents."

"No. I fetched your fishing tackle back. It's all right," said Dad. "Now what else is spoiled?"

"Oh, *you* know. I'll never grow. I'll never be ordinary. I just begin to think I can do things like everyone else, then BANG! Someone makes sure that I remember I'm a freak. I'll always be laughed at. Always."

"Does Dan laugh at you?" asked Dad.

"No."

"Did he ever laugh at you?" asked Dad.

"No. I suppose he felt sorry for me," mumbled Barty.

"Why should a great big teenager feel sorry for you? They are all busy, happy boys. They didn't have to bother with you at all, now, did they?"

"Why did they, then?" asked Barty, looking up at his Dad for the first time.

"I think," said Dad very slowly, "I think that they wanted to share something good with you and all the other juniors. They haven't just helped you, you know. What about the kids who come down from the new estate? Those town kids don't have such a nice life as you. The boys at the Canoe Club are just sharing their adventures. It's a bit like Charlie giving me bits for our van. He helps me, but he hasn't got a garden, so I give him home-grown things from my allotment. It's like your Mum cooking lovely food. She loves to cook and she's really good at it, so she likes to share it with people who don't have time to bake." Dad paused. "I think canoeing has made all those boys and girls very happy and they are just passing it on. Well, that's what *I* think."

Barty stared. His Dad was not known for long speeches. He was practical and could fix anything from a bumped knee to a broken car, but he rarely spoke at length. Dad himself was feeling very tired. He had had to think carefully to be able to talk to Mum and Barty without getting angry himself.

"I think I see," mumbled Barty, wiping away the tears with one hand.

"So you must learn to share," said Dad.

"I've got nothing to share," said Barty.

"Your environment," said Dad.

"What do you mean?" asked Barty, surprised by the long word.

"It's like your Miss Swan said—these city people envy you. You live here all the time. You have got to learn to let them come and enjoy it for the day."

"But they spoil everything. They smash things like my hide."

"The hide can easily be mended. They broke it and it made you angry for a while. But they can't learn if they don't come and visit, can they? And they don't know Barty in a canoe. They just saw a quaint little lad on *their* spot on the river. They

66

haven't seen you on *your* spot on the river. They haven't got your friends. They don't go to Canoe Club like you."

"I suppose not," said Barty. The tears were gone now. Dad was right of course. Barty felt a little better. Secretly he was glad about the fight. It proved he wasn't quite so easy to push around.

"As for that little matter of wandering off—" began Dad.

"Oh, Dad—" pleaded Barty.

"Your Mum and I are very disappointed that you broke the rules. When you fell in the river you could have been in real trouble if the water hadn't been so low. I bet those city boys couldn't swim. We could have lost you for good."

"Sorry," mumbled Barty, ashamed.

"You think about things till after tea," said Dad.

"Then?" said Barty hopefully.

"Then we're going up to the Canoe Club. We've got some work to do, I believe." Dad walked out of the bedroom.

Barty lay back on his pillow. All the tears had vanished. He was going to the barbecue after all.

11

The River's Song

Dad put the carefully-prepared food in the van with his tools and paintbrushes, and the Dobbs family drove to the club hut. Dad was in his oldest work overalls. Mum wore a flowery apron, and Barty wore his favourite dungarees with a clean T-shirt. Thinking what to wear to a working sort of party had worried Mum. Barty told her that everyone would be in really old clothes because the jobs were very dirty, but she felt they ought to look smart for the food afterwards.

"I've never been to a barbecue," she said. "Is it like the church garden party, but later at night?"

"Not exactly," laughed Barty. "You haven't seen the club hut."

When Mum arrived, she understood why Barty had laughed. The hut was like a large garden shed with racks inside for all the river canoes, the slalom canoes, paddles, buoyancy aids and helmets. There were tangled lifelines, broken paddles, poles for the 'gates' at slalom events, tattered flags and dirt from many years. The door hung off its hinges where someone had tried to break in. The roof tiles were broken where vandals had thrown rocks and the windows were grimy and cracked. The grassy space in front was full of weeds and knee-deep in litter. The steps down to the water's edge were slippery with moss and the car park looked like a building site, with half bricks, tin cans and bits of old rope scattered everywhere.

Mum surveyed the scene. "Well! No wonder you laughed at me, young Barty," she said. "I reckon we need more cleaning cloths and bags for the litter."

Dan's mum was there, and Mr and Mrs Greyson with the Terrible Twins, who weren't really terrible at all. In fact Eddie was the best friend Barty had ever made of his own age. Lots of other parents had turned up with their teenage children, along with some grown-ups who did a lot of touring by canoe and were also members of the Club. There was a group of Boy Scouts who used the hut and the canoes, and even two soldiers from the army garrison who enjoyed white water canoeing.

A man that Barty recognized from pool training sessions was giving out jobs. The twins' dad was to replace the broken windows. Someone else took the door right off to mend the hinges and split panels. All the canoes were put outside on the grass and carefully checked for damage. Then the repairs were listed. Everyone had a job to do. Mrs Greyson and Mrs Warren were heating the charcoal for the barbecue so Barty's Mum went to help them. Mrs Greyson seemed very expert at barbecues and soon was explaining to Mum what to do. They threaded pieces of lamb onto skewers with some chunks of vegetables, prepared the hamburgers, and stacked up a mountain of paper plates, along with the borrowed cutlery. Mum was in her element.

Barty's Dad was asked to look at the damaged roof as he used to be a builder. He reckoned it was going to be quite a long job but, armed with roofing felt, some new tiles and his tools, he climbed up to see what he could do. He felt very useful and happy, and was soon chatting away to his teenage assistant, explaining what he needed to do.

Barty looked at his parents. Well, they seemed to be working hard, so he went off with Eddie to do his share. They had been told to pick up every bit of litter, cut the grass and tidy the car park. They set to work with a will. Several other juniors were on the same task. Eddie teased Barty about being small enough to get down the holes made by water rats, but too small to lift the dustbin bags—but they were friendly jokes and Barty didn't feel angry any more. He would really miss Eddie when he went off to boarding school in September.

Everyone worked very hard and, as it got dark, delicious smells began to waft from the barbecue and the trestle tables were covered with good things to eat. One by one, the workers put away their tools and settled on the grass with their paper plates and cups. At first they just ate hungrily, for the hard work had given them all appetites. Someone began to play a guitar, and someone else began to sing. As the food gradually disappeared, other voices joined in the singing.

They sang camp fire favourites and old folk songs. One voice, clear and sweet, seemed to dominate the rest. On 'Land of the Silver Birch' this was the voice that took a solo on the verses, while everyone else hummed the chorus tune. To Barty's great surprise it was his mother singing. He knew she could sing, he supposed. She used to sing a lot when he was younger and she sang at church, but never like this. It sounded quite as good as on the television or the radio. She went on to sing 'Peace I Ask of Thee, O

River' and then 'Scarborough Fair' by herself. A young man sang 'Bridge Over Troubled Water' and everyone sang some sea shanties. Barty crept close to his Mum. She was red-faced from the heat of the charcoal, her hair looked like a badly made bird's nest and she was still dressed in her flowery apron. He leaned against her. Her arm went round him and she smiled down at him, but still she sang in the dark. The rubbish fire glowed like a proper camp fire in the centre of the circle of Canoe Club members on the grass.

The barbecue cooled down and the rubbish fire burned down to a safe glow of red ash. Tools and cleaning things were packed away, and Dad hoisted Barty onto his shoulders to carry him back to the van. Squashed together on the front seat, Barty said to his Mum, "I liked your singing. I didn't know you could sing like that."

Dad said, "Ah, she's not too bad, but you should have heard her mother, your grandmother. Now *she* was a one for singing, she was."

"That's right, Barty," said Mum. "My mother was Irish, and sang nearly all the time. Such a hard life she had, and yet she sang so sweetly and had a kind word for everyone."

"Why don't I know her?" asked Barty, thinking an Irish grandma sounded rather nice.

"Oh, she died years ago, before you were born. How she would have loved you, our Barty," said Mum.

12

Camping and a Slalom

Dad had to go back the next day to finish the roof of the hut. He had been quite right—there was too much work for one evening. He didn't take Barty, who was feeling very tired after his late night.

When he came back he said, "Dan was out on the river today. A few of them are going camping overnight to attend a novice slalom before they go back to school."

"That's nice," said Mum. "It will be good for them to have a change before the new term starts."

"That's what I thought," said Dad, "so I said Barty could go with them."

"You said WHAT?" demanded Mum.

"I said Barty could go and camp out so that he could be in the novice slalom. Eddie is going and some of the other juniors. Dan will be there, and Chris and John. You've met them all."

"Oh, I'm not worried about them. How could you be so stupid," shouted Mum. "It's not fair to upset Barty so."

"I haven't mentioned it to Barty yet. I told Dan that he had a bit of a problem. I also said, as far as I knew, he was nearly over it. We've had no bother this holiday, have we? Dan didn't care at all."

"But Barty cares. It would shame him so if he had an accident," said Mum, "and besides, he hasn't got any of the right things for camping."

"Dan has two of everything because his older brother used to go with him. He also has a small sleeping bag that he had when he was younger. He says Barty can have it and throw it away afterwards if he has to."

"Oh, well," said Mum in a bit of a huff, "if you and Dan have got things all sorted out, there's no point my saying anything, is there?"

"I told him I would have to ask you first. But you and I must agree before we tell Barty," said Dad.

"All right, then, tell me where it is and what happens," said Mum. Dad explained the plans. Eddie's dad was working on a children's adventure holiday scheme based at a boarding school just down the river. The children there had been learning canoeing as part of their holiday and, to end the course, they were having a simple novice slalom competition to which the Canoe Club had been invited, the older boys and girls to help, and the younger juniors to compete. Some were going to camp in the school grounds by the river bank and some were going by car the next day. The ones who camped were going to paddle down on the Friday, compete on the Saturday and paddle back on the Sunday. Dan said his mother was going to drive straight to the boarding school with all the equipment so that the canoeists only had to look after themselves. Mum went pale at the thought of a slalom, and the long paddle to get there. Dad said it was no worse than Barty's first river trip, and that the slalom was easier than paddling on the white water by the club hut. It was well-planned, and Barty was now safe in a canoe.

"But he's so little," she said.

73

"If he was in the Cub Scouts you would have let him go to camp," said Dad.

"I suppose so," said Mum.

"Dan says they camp out for most of the slalom competitions," said Dad. "If he is to try out the official competitions next year, you'll have to let him go then. Why not let him try it now at a small camp with friends, before a really big rally."

"If you think it's right," said Mum slowly. "I don't know what Dr Chowdhari would think."

"He'd think jolly good for Barty and jolly good luck."

So it was that when Barty came in from the back garden where he had been writing in his journal about the working barbecue party, his Dad told him he was going camping. Barty couldn't believe his ears at first. It couldn't be true! He was actually going camping with the big boys. He found it very difficult to swallow his tea.

"That's a fine start," said Mum. "If you don't eat properly you certainly can't go away on a trip."

Barty made an effort to eat his tea. After tea, he and his Dad walked up to the club hut to tell Dan it was all arranged that Barty could go camping and compete in the slalom. They met Tom on their way. He was just going down to the salmon hole.

"I'm going camping," said Barty, "in a canoe."

"Bit small to sleep in," remarked Tom seriously.

Barty giggled. "We're paddling the canoes to the camping place and then we're sleeping in tents."

"That sounds grand," said Tom.

There were eight of them going to camp out. Dan said that that was about the right number to keep everything organized. The girls were only going for the day so they would not be camping out. They had three tents to share. Barty didn't dare say he had never seen a tent close to before, except the big ones used at the church fête. He had never put one up. Words like 'ridge pole' and 'guy lines' and 'flysheet' meant nothing to him. He hoped he would learn quickly. Eddie had his own tent, which Barty was to share.

When they got home, Barty had a list of things that he had to take. Besides the small sleeping bag, he had to take some eggs, some bacon, some sausages, some bread, and anything else his Mum could spare. Dan said that because he was getting to know Barty's Mum, and he thought she would not let them starve if she could help it. He also had to have his toilet things and his old canoeing clothes, as well as some spare, clean, dry clothes.

Barty must have sorted his stuff out at least fifteen times by Friday. Mum had packed his food bag, slipping in some oatcake and some more of the parkin that everyone had seemed to like at the barbecue. Dad drove him to the club hut and they put his things into Mrs Warren's car. When Mrs Greyson arrived with Eddie, she looked at the big pile of things to take and offered to put some of them into her Volvo. Dad said he had nothing else to do. If it wasn't too far away, he could take the tents in his van.

Mrs Warren had been feeling a bit flustered, so she smiled in relief.

"Do you mind?" she asked. "It isn't far by road. I had no idea there was so much to carry for eight campers. What a good job they didn't have to fit it into canoes."

"I'll have to pop home and tell my wife," said Dad, "but I'll be back."

Barty's Mum was secretly quite pleased that Dad was going to the actual camp site. Now he would be able to make sure Barty settled in without seeming too fussy.

He soon returned to find Dan and Christopher sorting out the canoes. Barty had his favourite junior all-purpose canoe. Eddie was to have a full-sized one. Robert, the third junior, had his own canoe. The fourth junior was Peter Spurling. He was at secondary school, but had only started canoeing this summer, so he was also given a junior all-purpose canoe.

The canoes were in the water, and Dad had loaded up the camping equipment with Mrs Greyson and Mrs Warren; ground sheets, a cooker, tents, a gas cylinder, sleeping bags, clothing in kit bags, and other things the boys felt were useful were all there. The parents discussed their route to the holiday centre, while the paddlers set off. They had time for a cup of coffee, as they could do the journey quickly while the paddlers in their canoes would take hours on the twisting river.

13

The Holiday Centre

Dan led his flotilla of canoes down river. The children were happily laughing and joking, in a real holiday mood. Barty was near the end. He hoped he would be able to keep up. Behind him was Christopher, who was guarding the rear to keep an eye on the juniors. Barty paddled past the stretch of river where he and his father usually went fishing. There was the salmon hole, and the squashed hide. He thought he might build a better one for next summer. He was glad he hadn't hidden away after that fight.

Apart from giving Barty a different view of his familiar stretch of river, the paddle to the boarding school was uneventful and quite easy. As they approached the school, they saw a lot of canoes on the river. The other canoeists cheered and waved their paddles when they saw the Canoe Club group arriving. Eddie's dad waved from the bank.

"Is this the boarding school you are going to?" Dan asked Eddie, gazing at the beautiful old buildings and the playing field dotted with young athletes busy with all kinds of sporting activities.

"Yes," said Eddie. "My Dad works here, that's why. It's not always like this. This is just the holiday course."

They paddled into the bank. Mr Greyson showed them where they could put up the tents by a building, which was the school changing room and pavilion.

The parents with the tents were already there. The boys carried their canoes over to the camp site and if any of the holiday children thought Barty was odd, they were far too busy to say so. There were already some tents up.

"Camping is just one of the activities they can choose," said Eddie, feeling slightly in charge of the others. He had spent a lot of time here with his dad.

"Posh place, this," said Dad, as they came up. "Have you seen the main school house?"

"Eddie starts school here next week," said Barty.

"Would you like to go to boarding school, Barty?" asked Dad.

"No thanks," said Barty.

In spite of his fears, Barty was able to play his part in putting up the tents. He was told to hold tent pegs or pull on guy lines and to move himself. He was surprised at how big the tents were—they came out of such small bags.

While everyone set out their sleeping bags and gear, Mrs Warren organized the camping stove. She told Dan to be careful, to be sure to turn it off properly at night, to use an oven cloth for hot pans and to feed everyone properly.

"She sounds like my Mum," whispered Barty to Dad.

"Your Mum isn't the only worrier, you know," said Dad.

Mrs Warren stayed to cook their first meal of sausages and beans, as the boys were anxious to look at the weir on the slalom course.

"You give a lot of time to this sort of thing," said Barty's Dad, as he and Mrs Warren washed up. "It's very good of you."

"Well, I like to see them busy and happy. I like the Canoe Club gang, so I'm glad to help out. They could be knocking old ladies on the head or something dreadful."

Dad, thinking of the people who had tormented his son, was very thoughtful and agreed that the Canoe Club was worth a bit of time.

"They've been good to our Barty," he said.

"He's a nice boy. He's been very good for my son, you know."

Dad didn't really understand what she meant, but then they went off to find the boys. He saw Barty poised in a canoe at the top of a weir and sliding confidently over it. The two grown-ups left, calling that they would see the gang on Sunday. Dad thought he wouldn't give Mum precise details of what her little lad was doing.

The weir was really quite small as far as weirs go, but to a novice who hadn't tried one before it was big and rough enough. There were slalom gates at the top and bottom, and some others placed in the rough water around an island. Some of the gates had to be taken backwards, and none of them were to be touched by the paddles or the boat. Barty felt that if this was only a novice course, then he certainly wasn't quite ready for a full one. The holiday centre children were all inexperienced as well so he did not need to be too worried about making a fool of himself.

Barty went through the gates very carefully and slowly. Eddie rushed through very fast, hitting almost every gate. He grinned happily. He wasn't bothered.

When the whistles blew at the holiday centre the

children had to go to bed. Dan thought this was a good idea for his group too, and they hung their wet canoeing gear in the changing rooms on long clothes lines. Dan made hot chocolate for them all and then remembered what he had been told about the gas cylinder and turned it off. They settled down for the night. Barty thought he would never get to sleep. It didn't seem properly dark and he could hear Radio One from one of the other tents. Far away, an owl hooted. "Who?" it called. "Who?"

It's me, you silly old owl, thought Barty, it's me, Barty Dobbs, camping out with my friends for two nights.

"WHO—OO," said the owl, but Barty didn't hear him. He was fast asleep.

14

The Competition

They woke in the morning to the sound of whistles again. It was seven thirty. Eddie's father had told them to use the changing rooms in the sports pavilion for washing and showers along with the children from the holiday centre. The sports pavilion was a very interesting building with racks for boats and other equipment. There were some long thin boats like dragonflies. Barty was very curious about those. Dan said they were rowed by eight oarsmen at a time and went really fast. The boarding school was very keen on rowing.

Chris took a turn at cooking and had bacon and eggs sizzling in a pan for breakfast. "Did you have a good night?" he asked Barty.

"Yes, I slept like a log," replied Barty.

"No watery dreams?" asked Dan.

"What? Oh—no. No! Great!" Barty yelled and jumped around. He had slept peacefully and gone for a wash without even thinking about wet or dry nights. He hadn't even checked the sleeping bag.

"What is the song and dance for?" asked Christopher. "I only asked if he had had a good night."

"Barty always does a song and dance act in the morning, don't you, Barty," said Dan. He said nothing about wet or dry beds to Barty's great relief. His day was already perfect. He didn't care if it rained, or if it snowed, or if he fell in. He had

81

camped out with his friends and would be camping again with them tonight.

In fact, he didn't disgrace himself in the slalom. As he had practised the night before, he knew the way he had to go round. First he had to walk with his canoe on his shoulder to the start. Dan, Chris and the other seniors were judging. This meant they had to sit either at the start, the finish or by a gate to time each competitor, and to check that they went through the gates properly. They were linked by radio and so could start their stop watches at the same time. Each gate was numbered and had a big 'R' marked on it if you had to go through it backwards. Barty and the other juniors were on their own and had to stick their numbers on their canoes and make their way to the start on time by themselves. The juniors who had not camped out arrived in good time and got together to talk about their tactics.

As Barty was sticking his number on a white plastic circle on the canoe, he overheard some of the holiday children talking.

"You want to watch out for that little kid from the Canoe Club," said one. "Mr Greyson says he is ever so good."

"Which little kid?" said the other.

"You know, the one who looks about six. He's not. He's nearly ten and super in a canoe."

Barty was astonished. They had said nothing horrible—only admiring remarks about his skill in a canoe. He carried his canoe with pride to look at the notice board with the order of racing on it. A few competitors giggled as he went past. Some of the girls tried to fuss over him and help him but he brushed them away.

As the running order was alphabetical, Barty went among the first runs. He remembered last night. He had gone carefully, and hit no gates, but he had been very slow. Eddie had rushed at the course, hitting everything in sight, but had been fast. Barty knew he had to somehow strike a happy medium. On his first run, he went very carefully and neatly, but rather slowly. The gate at the bottom of the weir proved the hardest. The canoe was still bobbing wildly, having gone down the weir and it was quite hard to get it under control to go backwards through this particular gate—gate two. The other gates seemed fairly easy in comparison. Eddie and the other club juniors were yelling at him. Whether it was because he had gone wrong, or whether it was to make him go faster, he didn't know. He just paddled his best and finally came into the bank, puffing.

"Really good," said Eddie. "Smashing run. No penalties."

You got penalties (marks added onto your time) if you hit the gates with your paddle or canoe. Barty's time was not too fast but, as he had gone carefully, no marks were added.

Eddie tried to go fast and carefully. Like Barty, he had the most trouble at the foot of the weir, and scored penalties there as he hit the gate with his canoe. The Canoe Club juniors were better than the holiday children, but that was only to be expected. The holiday children had only had a week or a fortnight to train.

After a rest and lunch, cooked by Robert and

Peter, they all had a second run. The best times were the ones that counted. Barty thought he could risk a bit more speed. His first time had not been the best, but it had been quite good. He slid into the canoe and fixed his spray deck.

"Go it, Barty," yelled Eddie.

Barty thought of the children who had said how good he was. Yes, he'd go all right, fast as the silver fish in the river.

"Go! Go! Go!" yelled Eddie, as the starter nodded to Barty.

Go he did, with much more daring. He paddled as fast as he could, slid over the weir, hit the bottom and struggled to right himself ready for the bottom gate. Backwards through that, looking over his shoulder to watch the poles. One wobbled as he clipped it. On he went through the other gates. He didn't hit any others but he knew he would get penalties for gate two. He was so tired he could hardly believe it. His chest ached and his breathing felt very strained. In spite of the chilly water he was feeling hot. He came into the bank, his head pounding in time with his heart. He rested in the canoe, unable even to ask his time. He couldn't speak. He felt someone pat him on the back but he didn't know who it was.

The other competitors went in and the yells of encouragement went on. As Barty got his breath back he took more interest in the events. He pulled his canoe out of the water and went back to the tents for a drink. He was glad he didn't have a third run to do. He hung up his wet gear and returned to the river bank. He got cheery smiles and waves from the holiday children. He was that 'little kid' from the

Canoe Club and he didn't care. Dad was right. They had seen him in his element on the river and he had proved himself as good as them.

The times were being written in the boxes on the notice board. When Barty looked, his time was one of the best—better than Eddie's. He felt very proud, but he didn't dare talk about it, in case the magic went and he found himself last. People he didn't know kept patting him on the back or saying, "Jolly good." The day became a blur. He couldn't keep track of the times and his friends.

He decided to go and sit on the bank by the finish. The judge gave him a smile and then went back to his job. After the last novice had finished, the Canoe Club seniors gave a demonstration of all the different techniques used in slalom racing, and a firm that made canoes gave a demonstration of the different kinds of canoes and equipment you could buy. Then the final results were announced. Bartholomew Dobbs was fourth. Eddie was way behind him, about twelfth. Elaine had done better than Eddie. She was eighth. A Canoe Club member that Barty did not know well came first, and Peter Spurling was second. The holiday children did very well and everyone cheered and clapped.

All over the holiday centre the children had been having competitions in all the different sports. There had been archery, athletics, gymnastics, riding and show jumping, and swimming. The day had been like a mini Olympics. The holiday children were having a prize-giving and a disco after tea, to which the Canoe Club were invited. Barty had never been to a disco before and did not really like the idea. Dan said he had to go to collect his prize, so they all tidied up and went up to the main school hall. It had been decorated with balloons and streamers and a huge buffet tea had been laid out.

The director of the holiday centre made a speech thanking all the instructors who had given up their time. He thanked the Canoe Club and other groups who had helped with the competitions. He called the names of all the children who had done well enough to win prizes, and everyone clapped. The Canoe Club gave a cheer as Barty went up to collect a certificate for coming fourth.

★ ★ ★

A lot of the holiday children were feeling very sad. They had to go home to their towns and cities after the disco in buses or cars. They had had a lovely time in the country and by the river, and although the disco cheered them up for a while, some of the girls looked quite tearful. Everyone was swopping addresses and autographs, promising to keep in touch. Some of the staff and the older children were dancing, but the younger ones seemed to concentrate on talking and the food. Barty was flattered that a lot of the children wanted to talk to him and to have his autograph. He told them about his part of the river and about his Dad and the fishing. They really envied him and said so.

The hard exercise, the loud music of the disco and the strain of trying to talk made Barty very tired, and he was glad when the director made everyone sing 'Auld Lang Syne' and then sent them off to pack. The Canoe Club members who had just come for the day went off home. The parents came to fetch their holiday children, leaving the tired staff to clear up all the mess: they would not be going home for a day or two yet.

Dan's campers made their way back to the tents where they sat talking about the course and their results.

"Don't get conceited, Barty Dobbs," Dan said. "That was a special course, not a full slalom course; and you couldn't take part in an official slalom in a junior canoe, you know."

Barty looked disappointed. "Do you mean I'm not really any good after all?"

"No. I just mean that we have to get you trained in a full-size canoe this winter, ready to take on the world next year," said Dan.

"Hear! hear!" said Chris and the others.

"Next year," thought Barty. "Next year—" The river would still be there—and the canoes and his friends. He had never looked forward to a 'next year' so much.

"Goodnight," said Eddie. "You did really well."

Packing up the camp the next day was not nearly as much fun as setting it up, but eventually the last tent peg and the last pan were packed and the cars loaded. Barty's Dad was so proud of his son. He had realized that Barty enjoyed canoeing, but he had no idea that he was a possible slalom competitor. He had something to think about on his drive home while Barty and the gang paddled up against the current.

It was a tiring paddle home, but after the thrills of the day before it was very easy. Barty thought about the Canadian pioneers that Miss Swan had told them about, who had explored in canoes. He hadn't known then that one day he himself would go canoeing.

Thinking of Miss Swan reminded him of his journal. There was quite a lot more he had to write. As he paddled on, he planned out what he would draw and write.

The river journey passed successfully, but he was very tired again and glad to accept help in putting the canoe away. Dad and he were both very quiet on the drive home.

Mum wanted to know every detail about the camping and the slalom. She gave Barty a big hug when she saw the certificate. As she helped him to unpack, she felt pleased with him, but a little sad as well: her tiny boy was growing up.

15

Back to School

Barty's journal was so long that his mother had to buy him another notebook. He had a lot of photographs to stick in, as well as pages of writing and drawings to explain about the slalom and the camping. Mum looked very surprised by his pictures of the weir in the slalom course, for the swirling water looked very alarming to her. But Barty seemed so matter-of-fact about it, and about the way he had gone over the weir in his canoe. "If that was a novice course," thought Mum, "I dread to think what a harder course is like."

Barty thought that his journal was looking a bit tatty. The cover was loose because of all the extra bits he had stuck in it, and it was looking rather dirty.

"You've been writing in it almost every day for six weeks," said Mum. "Don't worry. It is better that it looks well used, but if you like I can find a bit of spare wallpaper to make a new cover." Barty covered the old and the new notebook to match with the wallpaper and wrote a new title on a sticky label. The notebooks looked a lot better then.

On the first day back at school, Barty gave in his journal. He was moved up into Mr Pugh's class, the top of the juniors, so Miss Swan wasn't his teacher any more. However, she smiled at him when she saw him in the playground and asked about his holiday. She said that she was very proud of him and wished him luck in the top class.

"I'll still come and do your tidying up for you," said Barty.

All the journals were put on a big table in the school hall. As well as the notebooks, there were all kinds of interesting souvenirs from the children's holidays. Ruth had brought in a Spanish doll in a gypsy costume. Nikki brought in a Welsh doll wearing the traditional black hat and check skirt, and carrying a broom. There was a pair of Dutch clogs, a lot of maps and postcards and even some models. One girl had been to Hadrian's Wall and she had made a model of a Roman fort from a kit. One of the boys had helped his dad restore old railway engines, and he had some photographs and a model engine. There were pressed flowers and sea shells, bottles of sand and dried sea weed. There was the biggest fir cone that Barty had ever seen from the South of France. It was a really interesting exhibition.

Every day at Assembly, Mr Roberts, the headmaster, chose something from the big table and asked the child who had brought it in to come out and talk about it. Some children became really tongue-tied standing in front of the whole school, but some were very good at speaking, and shared their holiday fun with everyone. Once Barty would have felt quite envious as he listened to tales of cross-channel ferries or of flying in an aeroplane. This year, he listened and enjoyed himself, but he knew that his holiday had been as good as theirs. However, Mr Roberts never called Barty out, and he thought that perhaps his journal was too untidy even to be noticed.

90

The competition was to be judged by one of the school governors, the Honourable Guy Vernon-Paget, who always came to the sports and everything. He seemed very shy with the children but wouldn't miss going into school for anything, even if he didn't know what to say when he got there. The teachers helped him to decide which was the best journal, but he made his own choice in the end, and kept it a secret.

The prizes were to be given at a special assembly to be held on Friday afternoon. Any parents who were free were asked to come into school to watch. As the local factories closed at two o'clock on Fridays, a lot of parents crowded into the school hall.

The whole school filed in, dressed in their best clothes for the occasion. The infants sat at the front on the floor, but the top juniors had chairs or PE benches. Mr Pugh made Barty sit on the end of his bench so that he could see the platform. The children buzzed with excitement as Mr Roberts came in with the Honourable Guy Vernon-Paget.

First of all the infants showed the big frieze they had made picturing all their holiday adventures, and some of them talked about what they had done. Everyone clapped politely at the carefully-rehearsed little speeches, as the blushing infants sat down. Then Mr Roberts spoke about the top juniors who had now gone on to the comprehensive school, and wished them luck at their new school. He called out the names of those who had won prizes for their hard work in the juniors before leaving and, looking very awkward in their new school uniforms, some old pupils came from the back to receive prizes from the Honourable Guy Vernon-Paget for work in English, maths, or just plain endeavour.

The Honourable Guy Vernon-Paget solemnly shook hands with them all and wished them luck in their new school. He took off his glasses, cleared his throat, and looked at the expectant children. The weather was still warm and he thought they looked like summer flowers in the garden, with the little girls in their best dresses and the boys in cool, coloured T-shirts.

"And now, the main reason for my visit," he said. "Hmm! The—hmm—Journal Competition."

An expectant murmur went round the hall. He picked up his glasses and polished them.

"Hmm... we have enjoyed all the entries. What a well-travelled lot of children you are. Ah—hem!" He paused again and looked round.

"Now I have read all the journals very carefully," he said, "and I think some are—hmm—very neat, very well written and carefully illustrated—hmm—"

Amanda looked all round. She knew that her handwriting was beautifully neat and that her drawings were colourful, if nothing else. She felt she was sure to win a prize.

"But," continued the Honourable Guy Vernon-Paget, "perhaps in a journal about your holidays, neatness—hmm—isn't everything, what?"

Brian Duffy cheered up. He knew his journal was very messy. He hated writing. But he had made a kite to show and it was quite good. It really flew. He had taken it to a kite-flying festival at the Honourable Guy Vernon-Paget's own house and grounds. Maybe, just maybe, he stood a chance of a prize after all.

"Hmm—er—you see, a very neat list of the places

you visited and the things you did—hmm—perhaps isn't quite enough."

Ruth panicked. Was her journal about Spain just a list? She had done what Miss Swan said and collected labels and things. Was it just a boring scrapbook after all? She felt sure it was a failure.

"Hmm—yes—" went on the Honourable Guy Vernon-Paget. Really, you would never think that he was boss of a huge factory with hundreds of workers and a farmer as well, thought his grown-up audience.

"Yes. So I looked for a journal that tried to convey something of the way of life in a particular place and was well observed. Some of you have been abroad, some of you stayed in England and some went to Wales. Some of you—ahem—had days out and some of you went away for weeks. Camping, caravanning, visits to grandparents—it has all been put down in the—um—books."

The children got fidgety and impatient. They looked at one another. The most important thing was WHO had won!

"One journal in particular gave me a lot of plea-sure—um—it was about a place I thought I knew well, but—um—in fact I learned some new things," said the Honourable Guy Vernon-Paget. The children sat up. "A place he knew?" they thought. "Where does he go for *his* holidays?"

"Um—this—er—um journal showed a sense of fun—adventure even—and besides—um—the young writer seemed to have learned new things to do. It's good to do something new on your holiday, isn't it? Um—" The children stared, waiting for him to get to the point. "Er—and the most remarkable thing is—um—that he did not travel more than six miles from his own home." The Honourable Guy Vernon-Paget looked relieved. He hated speeches and he'd got to the end of this one. The children fussed and stared, waiting. Amanda suddenly felt a horrible feeling in her stomach. She peered along the row to where Barty was quietly sitting.

"Now I really look forward to meeting—um," he paused to look at his paper, "Bartholomew Dobbs!"

Barty looked all round. Mr Pugh pushed him forward. The grown-ups clapped like mad and the school joined in. Miss Swan smiled like anything as Barty walked nervously forward to the platform.

The Honourable Guy Vernon-Paget had been warned about the size of his chosen winner. He himself was a tall, thin beanpole of a man. He looked down on Barty the way the heron looks down on his supper. He stretched out a long skinny arm and bony hand. He took Barty's and shook it warmly. "Well done, old chap. Congratulations. Remarkable." He smiled and his face lit up. His eyes twinkled. "I really enjoyed sharing your adventures."

Barty smiled up at him. Then he had to turn and face the whole school, who were still clapping like mad. Mr Roberts held up his hand.

"As you all know," he said, "I have been asking some of you writers to come and talk to us about your holidays. Now it is Barty's turn. He must tell us all about the best bit of his holiday."

Barty gulped. This was the last thing he had expected. The teachers smiled at him, waiting. Barty saw Amanda staring at him, open-mouthed.

"Well," he said slowly, pausing just like the Honourable Guy Vernon-Paget in his search for words, "um—it—it would be too long to tell you everything I did—um—but I think, yes, I think the best bit was going camping with my friends for two nights, and doing our own cooking and things, and going by canoe like real explorers. That was the best bit of all."

The teachers, the children and the parents clapped, with Mr and Mrs Dobbs clapping most of all. The Honourable Guy Vernon-Paget picked up a box.

"Hmm—for you—I hope you like it. It's a camera—it might help you with your wildlife photography, what? I'm interested in that myself, you know."

Barty looked into the box. There was a really modern camera, some rolls of film and a booklet about taking better pictures.

Mr Roberts shook his hand and Barty walked back from the platform to his place. He hardly noticed who got the second and third prizes, but he heard more clapping, and then it was time for refreshments. The school dinner ladies had done them proud. The hatch from which dinners were normally served was opened up, and the parents, friends, honoured guest and children were soon all tucking in to the delicious snacks and drinks.

The Honourable Guy Vernon-Paget spent some time talking to Barty's Mum and Dad. Mum was both embarrassed and proud. Talking about it afterwards she said she couldn't get over how natural, how kind and concerned for Barty, and how really interested in their way of life he was. She said he lost that hesitant speech when he was talking to just two people. He even invited Barty to go bird watching on his estate, and to take photographs, and he really *meant* it.

"I just don't get it," wailed Amanda Parsons. "I mean, what did you *do* all holiday to win a prize if you just stayed around home all the time? Did—did you really go camping?"

"Oh, I pottered about a bit by the river, and that," said Barty, grinning. "Yes, I really did have two nights camping with some boys from the comprehensive."

Amanda looked suspicious. "And did you...?" She saw the look in Barty's eye and didn't finish the sentence. She felt Barty was different somehow. He didn't look the same as when she had tormented him last term. She decided to go over to her mother.

Miss Swan kissed Barty. He went white, then red, then white again. Mr Pugh patted him on the back. They both looked as proud as Mr and Mrs Dobbs as they went off to get their tea together.

As for Barty, he felt a bit like crying, which was silly when he'd just got a prize.

★ ★ ★

The excitement of the prize giving was over and school settled into its usual routine, but Barty seemed to have won more than a prize for writing a journal. Children began to play with him and to talk to him, especially about canoeing.

Some boys from the other top class who also went to pool training spent hours discussing winter plans with him and re-living the summer's fun.

"It's going to be even better next year," said one of them. "We'll be getting some new canoes."

Next year, thought Barty, when he came home that night. Could any year ever be as good as this one? He stood watching the river in the autumn evening light before turning indoors, quite the most contented boy in the valley.